THE LIVERPOOL QUIZ BOOK

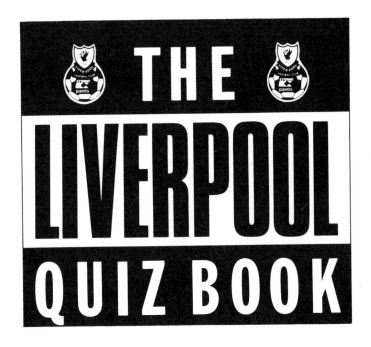

THE LIVERPOOL QUIZ BOOK

Compiled by
Alex Hosie

MAINSTREAM
PUBLISHING

First published in 1987 by
MAINSTREAM PUBLISHING COMPANY (EDINBURGH) LTD.
7 Albany Street
Edinburgh EH1 3UG

British Library Cataloguing in Publication Data:
Hosie, Alex
    The Liverpool Quiz Book.
    1. Liverpool Football Club — *(Association*
    Football) — Miscellanea
    I. Title
    796.334'63'0942753   GV943.6.L55

    ISBN 1 85158 094 8

Typeset in Ehrhardt by Pulse Origination, Edinburgh.
Printed and bound in Great Britain by Butler & Tanner, Frome, Somerset.

Contents

QUESTIONS

FLASHBACK 1986/87 11
SOME CLUB FACTS 11
REDS IN EUROPE 12
WHERE DID THEY COME FROM (1) 14
WHERE DID THEY GO ? (1) 15
REMEMBER THIS SEASON 1983/84 16
PICTURE QUIZ (1) 18
REDS IN THE FA CUP (1) THE EARLY YEARS 20
INTERNATIONAL REDS (1) 21
THE LEAGUE CAMPAIGNS (1) 22
MISCELLANEOUS (1) 23
REDS IN THE LEAGUE CUP (1) 24
PICTURE QUIZ (2) 28
REMEMBER THIS SEASON 1965/66 30
REDS IN EUROPE (2) 31
REDS IN THE FA CUP (2) INTO THE FIFTIES 32
THE LEAGUE CAMPAIGNS (2) 33
PICTURE QUIZ (3) 36
REMEMBER THIS SEASON 38
THE BACKROOM BOYS (1) 39
SOME EARLY HISTORY 40
PICTURE QUIZ (4) 43
REDS IN EUROPE (3) 44
WHERE DID THEY COME FROM (2) 45
WHERE DID THEY GO? (2) 46
PICTURE QUIZ (5) 50
REMEMBER THIS SEASON — 1922/23 52
REDS IN THE FA CUP (3) THE BUILDING YEARS 53
THE LEAGUE CAMPAIGNS (3) 54
MISCELLANEOUS 56
PICTURE QUIZ (6) 58
REMEMBER THIS SEASON — 1976/77 60
REDS IN EUROPE (4) 61
INTERNATIONAL REDS (2) 64
PICTURE QUIZ (7) 66
THE LEAGUE CAMPAIGNS (4) 68
REMEMBER THIS SEASON 1972/73 69
PICTURE QUIZ (8) 72

REDS IN EUROPE (5) 74
REMEMBER THIS SEASON — 1961/62 75
REDS IN THE FA CUP (4) THE SEVENTIES 76
INTERNATIONAL REDS (3) 77
PICTURE QUIZ (7) 80
MISCELLANEOUS (3) 82
REDS IN THE LEAGUE CUP (2) 83
THE LEAGUE CAMPAIGNS (5) 84
THE BACKROOM BOYS (2) 86
PICTURE QUIZ (10) 88
REDS IN THE LEAGUE SOME FIRSTS —
AND LASTS 90
REDS IN EUROPE (6) UP TO DATE 92
WHERE DID THEY COME FROM? (3) 94
WHERE DID THEY GO (3) 95
REMEMBER THIS SEASON 1946/47 96
REDS IN THE FA CUP (5) THE EIGHTIES 97
INTERNATIONAL REDS (4) 98
MISCELLANEOUS (4) 99
REDS IN THE LEAGUE CUP (3) 100
THE LEAGUE CAMPAIGNS (6) 101

ANSWERS

FLASHBACK 1986/87 107
SOME CLUB FACTS 107
REDS IN EUROPE (1) 108
WHERE DID THEY COME FROM (1) 108
WHERE DID THEY GO ? (1) 109
REMEMBER THIS SEASON 1983/84 110
PICTURE QUIZ (1) 110
REDS IN THE FA CUP (1) (THE EARLY YEARS) 111
INTERNATIONAL REDS (1) 111
THE LEAGUE CAMPAIGNS (1) 112
MISCELLANEOUS (1) 113
REDS IN THE LEAGUE CUP (1) 113
PICTURE QUIZ (2) 114
REMEMBER THIS SEASON 1965/66 114
REDS IN EUROPE (2) 115
REDS IN THE FA CUP (2) INTO THE FIFTIES 115
THE LEAGUE CAMPAIGNS (2) 116
PICTURE QUIZ (3)
.... 117

REMEMBER THIS SEASON 117
THE BACKROOM BOYS (1) 118
SOME EARLY HISTORY 118
PICTURE QUIZ (4) 119
REDS IN EUROPE (3) 119
WHERE DID THEY COME FROM (2) 120
WHERE DID THEY GO? (2) 120
PICTURE QUIZ (5) 121
REMEMBER THIS SEASON — 1922/23 121
REDS IN THE FA CUP (3) THE BUILDING YEARS 122
THE LEAGUE CAMPAIGNS (3) 123
MISCELLANEOUS 123
PICTURE QUIZ (6) 124
REMEMBER THIS SEASON — 1976/77 124
REDS IN EUROPE (4) 125
INTERNATIONAL REDS (2) 125
PICTURE QUIZ (7) 126
THE LEAGUE CAMPAIGNS (4) 126
REMEMBER THIS SEASON 1972/73 127
PICTURE QUIZ (8) 128
REDS IN EUROPE (5) 128
REMEMBER THIS SEASON — 1961/62 128
REDS IN THE FA CUP (4) THE SEVENTIES 129
INTERNATIONAL REDS (3) 130
PICTURE QUIZ (7) 130
MISCELLANEOUS (3) 131
REDS IN THE LEAGUE CUP (2) 131
THE LEAGUE CAMPAIGNS (5) 132
THE BACKROOM BOYS (2) 133
PICTURE QUIZ (10) 133
REDS IN THE LEAGUE SOME FIRSTS —
AND LASTS 133
REDS IN EUROPE (6) UP TO DATE 134
WHERE DID THEY COME FROM? (3) 135
WHERE DID THEY GO (3) 136
REMEMBER THIS SEASON 1946/47 136
REDS IN THE FA CUP (5) THE EIGHTIES 137
INTERNATIONAL REDS (4) 137
MISCELLANEOUS (4) 138
REDS IN THE LEAGUE CUP (3) 139
THE LEAGUE CAMPAIGNS (6) 139

Acknowledgements

We would like to thank Mr Gordon Whitehall for his assistance, and Mr Terry Mealy for providing many of the pictures.

While every care has been taken to ensure accuracy, the publishers and author cannot accept responsibility for any errors which may have occurred in this book.

Questions

1 Who scored Liverpool's goal in the 1986 Charity Cup final draw with Everton?

2 Who handed the Reds their first League defeat of the season?

3 Who left Liverpool for Glasgow Rangers at the end of the season?

4 Formerly on the books at Anfield he helped his team beat Liverpool 4-1 with a hat-trick. Who is the player?

5 Which Scottish club did Liverpool travel north to play a Centenary celebration match against?

6 Who put Liverpool out of the FA Cup?

7 What fee did Liverpool pay Oxford for John Aldridge?

8 In the third round of the Littlewoods Cup Steve McMahon hit a hat-trick as the Reds beat which team 4-1?

9 Who were the first team to win at Anfield in the League?

10 What record did Liverpool create in the Littlewoods Cup second round?

11 Who was named in his first international pool during the season as a replacement for an Anfield colleague?

12 Ian Rush started the League campaign with a double in the first match against which team?

13 What was the aggregate score in the Screen Sport Super Cup final against Everton, held over from the previous season?

14 Against which team did Ian Rush score the 200th goal of his career?

15 Which early League leaders did Liverpool thrash 6-2 at Anfield in a League match?

16 Striker Alan Irvine was signed from which Scottish team?

17 Who was in goals for Liverpool in the Charity Cup final?

18 Ian Rush was sent off for the first time in his career after the close of the first League match at Anfield against which team?

19 Which chief scout left Anfield, and who replaced him?

20 Who scored a hat-trick of penalties in the Littlewoods Cup against Coventry?

21 Who is the Liverpool Club Secretary?

22 What is the record attendance at Anfield, and who were the visitors?

23 What is Liverpool's record win?

24 What is the worst defeat the Reds have suffered?

25 Who has made most League appearances for Liverpool?

26 What is the highest amount of League points the Reds have gained in a season?

27 What is the most goals Liverpool have scored in a League season?

28 In which year did Liverpool first win the FA Cup?

29 In which year did Liverpool first win the first division?

30 In which year did Liverpool first win the League Cup?

31 In which year did the Reds first play in European competition?

32 Who was Liverpool's first manager?

33 In which year did the Reds win the European Super Cup?

34 How many European finals have Liverpool played in?

35 In which year did Liverpool first play in the first division?

36 How many times have Liverpool won the League championship?

37 How many seasons have Liverpool spent in the second division?

38 Who were the first team to play a competitive match at Anfield against Liverpool?

39 In which four years were Liverpool beaten FA Cup finalists?

40 Who were Liverpool's first ever opponents in the Screen Sport Super Cup?

REDS IN EUROPE (I)

41 Who were the opposition when John Wark hit a hat-trick at Anfield in the 1984/85 European Cup?

42 When Liverpool beat Oulu Palloseura 10-1 at Anfield in the 1980/81 European Cup, which two players got hat-tricks?

43 When Kevin Keegan scored his first European goal at Anfield, who were the opposition?

44 Who has made most appearances in Europe for Liverpool?

45 In his only European tie for Liverpool, he scored the club's first Euro goal. Who was he?

46 Against which team did Ray Clemence make his European debut?

47 When Liverpool won the European Cup for the first time in

Phil Neal, former Liverpool captain, in action.

1977, who scored their first goal in the tournament?

48 Who were the opposition when Anfield housed its biggest ever European crowd of 55,104?

49 When Liverpool beat Celtic 2-0 at Anfield in the semi-final of the 1965/66 Cup Winners Cup, which two players got the goals?

50 Who were the first team to beat Liverpool at Anfield in European competition?

51 In their first season in Europe Liverpool got to the semis of the European Cup. Who eliminated them?

52 In the 1966/67 European Cup Liverpool needed a playoff to beat which team in the preliminary round?

53 In round two of the 1967/68 Fairs Cup Liverpool won the first leg by 8-0 at Anfield only to lose the second leg 2-1. Against which team?

54 Who wore the number 2 jersey in both legs of the 1968/69 Fairs Cup against Atletico Bilbao, when the Reds lost on the toss of a coin?

55 In the 1969/70 Fairs Cup what was the score in the first round second leg tie away to Dundalk?

56 What record was set by Roger Hunt in his first European season, 1964/65?

57 Name the two Reds full-backs who missed both legs of the 1965 European Cup semi-finals against Inter Milan?

58 Who scored an own goal when Liverpool lost the 1965 Cup Winners Cup final after extra time to Borussia Dortmund?

59 Against which team did Emlyn Hughes score his first European goal?

60 Who did Liverpool beat on the toss of a coin in the 1964/65 European Cup?

WHERE DID THEY COME FROM? (I)

61 From which Scottish team did the Reds sign Alan Hansen?

62 What Scottish Junior side did Billy Liddell play for before being called up to Anfield?

63 Jack Balmer was signed as an amateur from which club?

64 Where did Peter Cormack play before coming to Anfield?

65 Which player was signed from Scunthorpe to take over the centre-half position from Laurie Hughes?

66 Phil Neal spent six years with which small team before Bob Paisley snapped him up?

67 With which Irish Junior team did the great Elisha Scott play before he came to Liverpool?

68 Eph Longworth played for another Lancashire club before Liverpool. Can you name the club?

69 Where did James Bradley come from in 1905?

70 Name the team he left and the fee Liverpool paid when Tony Hateley came to Anfield?

71 The last player signed by Bill Shankly cost £180,000. Who was he and which team did Liverpool buy him from?

72 Billy Dunlop, a great Reds full back for 15 years around the turn of the century, started his career with which Scottish team?

73 With which club did Terry McDermott play before Newcastle?

74 Where did former captain and manager Phil Taylor start his playing career?

75 From which team did Liverpool sign Tony Rowley?

76 Jimmy MacDougall, the thirties half-back, came to Anfield from which Scottish team?

77 Matt Busby joined the Reds from which club?

78 Willie Fagan, on Liverpool's books for 15 years, joined the Reds from which team?

79 With which non-League team did Jimmy Case once play?

80 In 1973 Liverpool paid £200,000 for him and he had to wait three years for his chance at Anfield. Who was the player, and from which club did he join Liverpool?

WHERE DID THEY GO? (I)

81 Frank McGarvey left Liverpool after failing to find a first-team place. Where did he go?

82 Name the 20's inside right and England internationalist who left Liverpool in the twilight of his career for West Bromwich Albion.

83 Andy McGuigan was the first man to score five in a League match for Liverpool. Which club did he join on leaving Anfield?

84 Where did Roger Hunt continue to score after he left Anfield?

85 Name the club he went to and the fee involved when Graeme Souness left Liverpool.

86 Jimmy Ross, a star forward in the last century, continued to play senior football with which club after Liverpool?

87 With which Irish team did Geoff Twentyman take the job of player/manager?

88 After nearly 20 years at Anfield Donald McKinley left for pastures new. Where?

89 What club did Avi Cohen join on leaving the Reds?

90 What career did twenties captain Jimmy Jackson take up when he left football?

91 Chris Lawler left Anfield in 1975 to team up with which old mate at which club?

92 When goalkeeper Bob Bolder found stony pickings in the Liverpool first team, where did he head for?

93 Can you name the year, the fee and the club he went to when Jimmy Melia left the club?

94 In 1902 the brilliant Scottish internationalist John Walker returned to his native land. Which team did he join?

95 Name the non-League club Willie Fagan joined in 1952 as player/manager?

96 In which year did Gordon Milne leave Anfield to go to Blackpool?

97 At the end of 1959, which club did Louis Bimpson join?

98 Fifties forward John Evans went south a bit after leaving Liverpool. Where did he go?

99 After almost 300 appearances in a Liverpool jersey, this twenties stalwart left the club to play for Wolves. Can you name him?

100 Name two senior clubs Brian Hall played for after his Liverpool days were over?

REMEMBER THIS SEASON—1983/84

Again Liverpool had the Kop singing with another record-breaking title win and a fourth triumph in the European Cup, unprecedented in British football. Liverpool had by now earned the right to be called Europe's team of the decade. How much can you remember about the season?

101 In which League match did Ian Rush hit five out of six for Liverpool?

102 Who finished second in the League to Liverpool?

103 Who scored in the fourth round of the Milk Cup against Birmingham to earn Liverpool a 1-1 draw and a replay?

104 Who scored the first goal of the Reds' European campaign against BK Odense?

105 Who did the Reds beat 4-0 in the FA Cup third round at Anfield?

106 Apart from Bruce Grobbelaar, who else played all League games without scoring a goal?

107 Who did Liverpool beat 8-1 on aggregate in the Milk Cup second round?

108 Which second division team took the Reds to a replay in the fifth round of the Milk Cup?

109 Near the end of the season, against which team did Ian Rush hit four out of five goals in a League match?

110 Who put Liverpool out of the FA Cup?

111 In the semi-final of the Milk Cup Liverpool beat Walsall 4-2 on aggregate. Who got three of those goals?

112 Which two players appeared as substitutes in the European Cup final as replacements for Dalglish and Robinson?

113 What was Graeme Souness's last game at Anfield for Liverpool?

114 Liverpool won the League with a 0-0 draw in the second-last game on the season. Where?

115 When the Reds beat Everton 1-0 in the Milk Cup final replay, who scored the goal?

116 Which third division side took the Reds to three games in the Milk Cup?

117 What was the score in the fourth round replay in the Milk Cup against Birmingham at Anfield?

118 Who scored most League goals after Ian Rush, and there are two players?

119 Who made a scoring debut at Watford in the League in March 1984?

120 Name the team which won the European Cup for the fourth time?

17

121 No bother here. Name the player?

122 From which team did Liverpool sign him?

123 In what year did he make his Liverpool debut?

124 Against which country did he win his first cap?

125 In 1893/94 Liverpool played their first Cup-tie proper and won 3-0. Who were the opposition?

126 In 1901/02 the Reds met Everton in the Cup for the first time, and won 2-0 after a draw. Who scored those two goals?

127 In 1884/85 the Reds had to replay a Cup-tie when there was a protest, but they still won. Who was the match against?

128 How many times did the Reds play Sheffield United in the semi-final of the 1898/99 FA Cup?

129 In the semi-final of 1905/06 who beat Liverpool 2-0?

130 In 1908/09 Liverpool beat Lincoln 5-1 in the first round. Who scored a hat-trick on his Cup debut in that game?

131 In 1892/93 which team did Liverpool beat 9-0 in a qualifying round?

132 In 1910/11 which famous Liverpool player made his Cup debut in a second round defeat by Everton. He was a right-back?

133 Who scored Liverpool's first goal in the Cup proper?

134 In 1897 the Reds reached the semi-final for the first time but lost 0-3 to Aston Villa. Where was the match played?

135 In the 1897/98 Cup Liverpool lost 1-5 in a third round replay to which team.?

136 When the Reds reached the 1897 semi-finals which two first division teams did they beat to get there?

137 In the 1908 Cup when the Reds lost 1-3 to Newcastle who scored his only Cup goal for Liverpool in that game?

138 1906 was the first time Liverpool met a London club in the Cup. Who were they?

139 In the 1903 and 04 Cups Liverpool went out at the first attempt, but which player scored in both those defeats to make him the only Liverpool player to score in the Cup for three years.?

140 In 1893, their first season, who beat Liverpool in the third qualifying round of the Cup?

141 Who beat the Reds in the first round of the 1910 Cup?

142 In the fourth round of the 1906 Cup Liverpool got their first

Cup hat-trick against Southampton. Who scored it?

143 In 1899 Liverpool lost the marathon semi-final to Sheffield United. At which ground was the tie finally decided?

144 In 1894 Liverpool met first division opposition for the first time in the Cup and beat them. Who were they?

INTERNATIONAL REDS (I)

145 Who was capped twice for Scotland while at Anfield and never played in the Liverpool first team?

146 Against whom did Tommy Smith receive his only England cap?

147 Name the three Liverpool players who made their England debuts in the same game against Wales at Wrexham in 1976?

148 Who was the last Liverpool player to score on his England debut?

149 Against whom did Kenny Dalglish receive his first Scotland cap as a Liverpool player?

150 Alex Raisbeck won eight Scotland caps. How many were against England?

151 Steve Heighway was capped once for Eire after leaving Liverpool. What club was he with?

152 Against whom did Joey Jones score his only goal for Wales, and what club was he with at the time?

153 Against which country did Jim Beglin receive his first Eire cap?

154 Which Liverpool player played in seven wartime internationals against England?

155 Who was the first Liverpool player to be capped for Scotland?

156 He won only two caps for England, both in 1963, and scored in one match against Switzerland as England won 8-1. Who?

157 Which unlikely Red scored on his England debut against Malta at Wembley in 1971?

158 Which Liverpool player had to wait 11 years between his first cap and his fourth and last cap?

159 In Phil Neal's 50th and last cap for England he was on the losing side at Wembley. Who beat England 1-0 in that match?

160 How many Liverpool players played in the 1970 World Cup Finals?

21

161 What record for England did Sam Hardy set in 1910 that wasn't beaten until 1938?

162 Who was the first Liverpool player to be capped for England?

163 Which Red scored on his England debut against Northern Ireland in 1957?

164 Name the two famous Liverpool players who made their England debuts together against Wales in Cardiff in 1972?

THE LEAGUE CAMPAIGNS (I)

165 When Liverpool were relegated in 1954 who went down with them?

166 Which team did Liverpool beat to clinch the second division title in 1962?

167 In 1954 who scored a League hat-trick in the space of five minutes against Port Vale?

168 In 1963/64 who was the last player to score four in a League match *against* Liverpool?

169 What is the lowest points total the Reds have gained in the League?

170 In which match did Kenny Dalglish hit his 100th goal for Liverpool in October 1981?

171 Who were Liverpool playing when Kevin Keegan made his League debut at Anfield in 1971?

172 In 1982/83 West Bromwich fielded two different keepers in their League matches with Liverpool. Can you name them?

173 Against which team did Jim Beglin make his debut in 1984?

174 In 1947 who did Liverpool beat in the last game of the season, away from home, to win the League title?

175 There were a few records set in 1953/54, and one was Liverpool's highest ever goals against tally. What was it?

176 Who was top League scorer in 1960/61 season?

177 Who were second to Liverpool when they won the League in 1964?

178 Who made his only first team appearance in a League match in 1973/74 at Birmingham and was substituted by Brian Hall?

179 When Liverpool won the League in 1976 who scored seven goals but only started five games, including his debut at Middlesbrough?

180 Which youngster scored on his debut in 1978 at Anfield against Leicester after coming on as a substitute?

181 In 1979 the title came back to Anfield with the Reds setting a new goals against record. What was it?

182 In 1926 this 'Demon's' League record was played one scored one. Who was he?

183 Where did Liverpool finish in the League in 1919/20, the first season after the First World War?

184 In which League did Liverpool first play?

MISCELLANEOUS (I)

185 Which player played for Everton in the first division and Liverpool in the second division?

186 Who was Bob Paisley's first signing for Liverpool?

187 Who was captain of the Arsenal team which beat Liverpool in the 1950 FA Cup final?

188 Where and when did Kenny Dalglish grab his first goal for Liverpool?

Old pals — Bob Paisley side by side with John Toshack.

189 Ian Callaghan made his Liverpool debut in 1960 as a replacement for which great Reds player?

190 Terry McDermott was on the losing side five times at Wembley. When was his first success?

191 Who made his Liverpool debut when he was rushed to Goodison to play against Everton instead of playing in a Reserve match?

192 Who captained Borussia Munchengladbach in the 1977 European Cup final against Liverpool?

193 Who captained Bruges in the 1978 European Cup final at Wembley against Liverpool?

194 Bruges' manager took his team to the 1976 UEFA Cup final and the 1978 European Cup final against Liverpool. Who was he?

195 Who was Liverpool's first £100,000 teenager?

196 How did Graeme Souness get on the winning side on his first appearance at Anfield?

197 Which Liverpool player was a junior volleyball internationalist?

198 What job did former keeper Steve Ogrozovic do before playing football professionally?

199 Who took over as captain of Liverpool from Emlyn Hughes?

200 In season 1979/80 who was top scorer in Liverpool's reserve team?

201 Who provided the opposition to Liverpool in Ray Kennedy's 500th senior game?

202 In 1979/80 the first three in the PFA Player of the Year Awards were Liverpool players. Can you name them?

203 Which former Scottish internationalist had a testimonial match at Anfield but never played for Liverpool?

204 In the 1975 Charity Shield who wore the number 12 jersey for Liverpool and played in the full match.?

REDS IN THE LEAGUE CUP (I)

205 Liverpool drew 1-1 at Anfield in their first ever League Cup match with Luton in season 1960/61. Who scored for the Reds?

206 In the second round in 1975/76 a penalty in 88 minutes gave Liverpool a 1-0 win over York. Who scored it?

Souness, Neal, Dalglish, McDermot, Hansen and Johnston celebrate another king Kenny goal.

207 In 1977/78 Liverpool won a fifth round tie at Wrexham by 3-1. Who scored a hat-trick in that game?

208 In the 1978 final against Nottingham Forest David Fairclough appeared as a substitute in both matches. Which two players did he replace?

209 In the 1979/80 Cup, who did Liverpool beat in the fourth round by 2-0 thanks to a David Fairclough double?

210 In the 1980 semi-final first-leg against Nottingham Forest, what was the score?

211 In the 1981 semi-final second leg at Anfield against Manchester City Liverpool drew 1-1. Who scored a brilliant goal in that game?

212 In the 1981/82 Cup, which team did Liverpool trounce 11-0 on aggregate in the second round?

213 What was the 1982 semi-final aggregate score against Ipswich?

214 In the third round of the 1982/83 Cup who did Liverpool beat 1-0 and who scored the goal on his League Cup debut?

215 In the 1983 final who got the extra time goal to give the Reds the Cup by 2-1?

216 In the 1983/84 Cup Liverpool replayed the fourth and fifth rounds, and won them both 3-0. Who were the two opposing teams?

217 Who beat Liverpool 1-0 in the third round of the Cup in 1984/85?

218 In the 1985/86 Cup what was the score in the second round tie away to Oldham?

219 Who scored for West Ham in the replayed final of 1981 which Liverpool won 2-1?

Alan Kennedy and Phil Thompson show the fans the Charity Shield.

220 In the 1980/81 Cup who did Liverpool beat 4-1 in the fourth round?

221 In the 1985/86 Cup who beat Liverpool 5-2 on aggregate in the semi-finals?

222 In the 1960/61 Cup who beat Liverpool in the third round?

223 In 1970/71 which team took Liverpool to a replay and extra time in the second round before the Reds won 3-2?

224 Against which team did Kevin Keegan score his first League Cup goal for Liverpool in 1972/73?

225 Name this former Anfield hero?

226 How much did Liverpool pay for his services?

227 In which year did he join Liverpool?

228 Against which country did he make his international debut?

Liverpool won the League championship for the second time since their return from the second division and in only their second season in Europe they reached the Cup Winners Cup final. A great season at Anfield as the rebuilt team went from strength to strength.

229 Liverpool won the League using the smallest amount of players ever in a League campaign. How many players were used?

230 What was the score when Everton visited Anfield in 1965 in the League?

231 Which player missed both Cup Winners Cup semi-final ties against Celtic, the only European games he missed in five years from 1964-69?

232 In the Cup Winners Cup final who scored Borussia Dortmund's first goal?

233 Who was captain of the club during the season?

234 He scored in a 2-2 draw with West Brom, his second and last League goal although he played 274 League games for Liverpool. Who?

235 Five players were ever-present in the League while Ian St John missed only one match. Who took his place against Blackpool?

236 Liverpool went out of the FA Cup at Anfield in round 3 to which team?

237 Liverpool used their first substitute in League football against West Ham at Anfield and he scored. Who was he?

238 How did Roger Hunt's season finish with a major award?

239 Who would normally take penalties for the Reds at that time?

240 His only game of the season was against Celtic in the Cup Winners Cup in Glasgow. Who?

241 Peter Thompson scored his first European goal against which team?

242 Which English club did Borussia Dortmund beat in the Cup Winners Cup semi-final to go through to the final against Liverpool?

243 Not a forward, he played only 28 League games and was third top goalscorer. Who was he?

244 Who beat Liverpool in their first home League match of the season?

30

245 Roger Hunt scored a double at Anfield as Liverpool clinched the League title by beating which team?

246 In the preliminary round of the Cup Winners Cup against Juventus at Anfield, the Reds won 2-0. Which two players scored the goals?

247 It was their only season in the first division, but they managed to hold Liverpool to a 0-0 draw. Who?

248 Name the team which played in the club's first European final?

REDS IN EUROPE (2)

249 When Liverpool were involved in a play-off against Cologne in the 1964/65 European Cup, where was it played?

250 What was the score when Liverpool played Dundalk at Anfield in the 1969/70 Fairs Cup?

251 Who beat Liverpool 5-1 in the first leg of their 1966/67 European Cup first round tie?

252 When Liverpool beat Inter Milan 3-1 in the first leg of the 1965 European Cup semi-final at Anfield, who scored for Inter?

253 Where did Liverpool play in the 1966 Cup Winners Cup final?

254 Against which team did Emlyn Hughes make his European debut?

255 Who did Liverpool beat in a preliminary round of the 1965/66 Cup Winners Cup?

256 Who were the opposition in Liverpool's first European final?

257 When Liverpool beat Malmo 2-0 in the first round, first leg of the 1967/68 Fairs Cup, who got a double for the Reds?

258 What was the score in Hungary against Ferencvaros in the third round first leg of the 1967/68 Fairs Cup?

259 Who put Liverpool out of the 1967/68 Fairs Cup?

260 Who played centre-forward in the 1964/65 European Cup first round first leg tie in Reykjavik and scored his only European goal?

261 Who scored the two goals when Liverpool beat Honved 2-0 in the quarter-final of the 1965/66 Cup Winners Cup at Anfield?

262 Who scored the goal in the first leg of the 1973 UEFA Cup semi-final when Liverpool beat Spurs 1-0?

263 Who did Liverpool beat in the quarter-finals of the 1971 Fairs Cup?

264 In the 1975/76 UEFA Cup Liverpool beat Hibernian 3-1 at Anfield to win 3-2 on aggregate. Which player scored a hat-trick?

265 In the final of the 1975/76 UEFA Cup Liverpool were losing 2-0 to Bruges at Anfield in the first leg, but scored three in five minutes in the second half to win. Name the three players who scored?

266 Who did Liverpool beat in the first round of the 1971/72 Cup Winners Cup after losing the first leg 2-1?

267 What was the first European trophy Liverpool won, and in what year?

268 Who made his only European appearance for the Reds in the 1969/70 Fairs Cup second round at Anfield?

REDS IN THE FA CUP (2)
INTO THE FIFTIES

269 In 1913 Arthur Metcalfe hit a second round hat-trick as Liverpool won 4-1 away from home against which famous club?

270 In the last Cup game the Reds played before the Second World War, they lost 4-1. Who beat them?

271 In 1948 Manchester United beat Liverpool in the Cup. It was United's home tie, but where was it played?

272 In the 1949 Cup, who scored in the last seconds of a first round tie against Nottingham Forest to get Liverpool extra time and a replay?

273 In the 1950 Cup final, who scored Arsenal's two goals against the Reds?

274 In 1914 Liverpool beat Villa 2-0 in the semi-final at which ground?

275 In the years 1930/31 and 32 Liverpool went out of the Cup in the early stages all at Anfield, but which three teams beat them?

276 Who did Liverpool beat in the 1950 Cup semi-finals?

277 In 1946, why did Liverpool play Chester and Bolton twice in the Cup even though they beat one team and lost to the other?

278 In their first Cup-tie after the First World War, which unlikely team took Liverpool to a first round replay?

279 Why was Liverpool's second Cup final in 1950 a bit special?

280 In the 1948 Cup first round replay against Nottingham Forest, what was the score?

281 Who scored the goal for Burnley in the 1914 Cup final when the Reds went down 0-1?

282 In 1947 who beat Liverpool in a semi-final replay?

283 When Liverpool reached the Cup final in 1914 they had to replay their first round tie. Who were the opposition?

284 Which team held an early Cup hoodoo over Liverpool and put them out of the tournament four times in 16 years from 1908 to 1924?

285 In the fourth round of the 1934 Cup, which team gave up home advantage to Liverpool and lost 3-1?

286 In the 1950 Cup Liverpool were taken to a third round replay before going through 2-1. Against which team?

287 In 1924, 25 and 26 Liverpool met the same team in the Cup and got through twice on replays, losing the other time. Who were the team?

288 In the 1935 Cup which non-League team did Liverpool beat 6-2?

THE LEAGUE CAMPAIGNS (2)

289 Where did Graeme Souness make his League debut for Liverpool?

290 In 1981/82 how many straight wins did Liverpool have late in the season to win the League?

291 In 1982/83 Ian Rush got four in one League match and three in the next. Name the two opposing teams?

292 In 1984/85 the Reds finished second in the League on goal difference to which club?

293 In 1968 Alun Evans scored on his League debut for Liverpool in a 4-0 win at Anfield. Who were Liverpool playing?

294 With 12 goals John Toshack was top League scorer in 1974/75. How many games did he play?

295 Why was the 1976/77 title so special in terms of records?

296 In 1985/86 who were the only team to win at Anfield in the League?

297 In 1981/82 Liverpool won the League by beating Spurs at Anfield. What was the score?

298 The first goal of Liverpool's 1984/85 League campaign was an own goal. Who scored it, and the clue is it was against Norwich?

299 In 1978/79 only four teams scored at Anfield in the League. How many can you remember?

300 On Boxing Day 1963 Roger Hunt hit four out of six at Anfield against which team?

301 Tony Hateley's last League goal for the Reds was in August 1968 in a 4-1 win at Anfield over who?

302 Young Phil Thompson came into League football as a substitute for John Toshack in 1972 at which ground?

303 Name the young player who made his debut in the second game of 1982/83 against Birmingham and did not play another League match for five months?

304 Liverpool won the 1983 Championship but finished badly. How many of their last games were without a win?

305 In 1894 Liverpool won promotion to the first division with a 2-0 Test Match win over Newton Heath. Who were the two Liverpool scorers?

306 Who came into the team late in the 1903/04 season, got five goals in nine games, finished top scorer the next season and stayed for nine years?

307 In 1968/69 he played his last League game for Liverpool, his only one of that season, and he scored against Wolves. Who was he?

308 Apart from Ray Clemence, who else played all League matches in 1975/76?

John Toshack and Steve Heighway provide a podium for the jubilant Keegan.

309 Who is this player?
310 In which country was he born?
311 From which team did Liverpool sign him?
312 In which country did he first play senior football?

Liverpool won the European Cup for the third time, and also won the League Cup, a trophy they were to keep at Anfield for four successive seasons. New players had come to the club and had helped keep the Anfield traditions great. See what you remember.

313 Who finished top League scorer for Liverpool?

314 The Reds had their lowest League finish for ten years. Where were they placed at the end of the season?

315 When Ian Rush made his League debut for Liverpool what jersey did he wear, and who were the opposition?

316 The second goal in three seasons for this young player was in the League Cup against Swindon. Who?

317 In the first leg of the League Cup semi-final against Manchester City Liverpool won 1-0 at Maine Road. Who scored the goal?

318 Against which team did Ian Rush make his European debut?

319 Name the defender who bowed out at Brighton after only 18 League appearance in two seasons?

320 This youngster's only first-team game came in the League at the tail end of the season against Sunderland when he came on for Howard Gayle at Anfield. Who was he?

321 The League Cup campaign started with a shock defeat by which team?

322 Which three players played in the second leg of the European Cup semi-final against Bayern Munich but took no part in the final?

323 Ronnie Whelan's League debut was his only game of the season and he scored. Who were Liverpool playing?

324 Who scored Liverpool's first goal in the European Cup campaign?

325 Who played his last game for Liverpool in the European Cup semi-final against Bayern Munich at Anfield?

326 For the first time in eight years a player scored in the first and last League matches of the season. Who was the player?

327 Who did Liverpool beat in the third round of the FA Cup by 4-1?

328 Who did the Reds beat 3-1 in the fifth round of the League Cup?

329 His only full game in the League for Liverpool was against Birmingham, but he became better known elsewhere. Who?

330 When Kenny Dalglish missed a League match against Ipswich during the season, why was it significant?

331 When Liverpool and West Ham drew 1-1 in the League Cup final in the first game, who scored for the Reds?

332 Who put Liverpool out of the FA Cup in the fourth round?

THE BACKROOM BOYS (I)

333 For how long was John McKenna manager of Liverpool?

334 Which former Reds manager captained West Ham in the first Wembley FA Cup final?

335 Name the Liverpool coach who was appointed manager when Don Welsh was dismissed?

336 Who was the first player to make his Liverpool debut under the management of Bill Shankly?

337 What trophies did Liverpool win in Bob Paisley's first season as manager?

338 Of whom did Bob Paisley say 'He says all his goals are lucky until it's time to renew his contract'?

339 Joe Fagan was trainer of which team before joining the Anfield backroom staff?

340 How many times did former manager Phil Taylor play for Liverpool?

341 Which Scottish Junior team did Kenny Dalglish play for?

342 Name the club director who was appointed manager in 1923?

343 Who became manager of Liverpool after W E Barclay?

344 Who took over as manager of the club from George Patterson?

345 Which manager gave Ronnie Moran his first-team chance with Liverpool?

346 Name four other senior teams managed by Bill Shankly?

347 Who was the last player Shankly bought for Liverpool?

348 How many times was Bob Paisley named as Manager of the Year?

349 What did Joe Fagan do in his first season as manager that no other English club manager had done?

350 Who was the trainer of the team that won the League in two successive years, 1921/22 and 1922/23?

351 What other job did W E Barclay hold as well as manager of Liverpool?

352 Name the man who was the founder of Liverpool FC?

SOME EARLY HISTORY

353 Where and when did the first Merseyside derby take place?

354 Where was the 1914 Cup final, Liverpool's first, played?

355 He played in the first Liverpool team to play in senior football and later became a director of the club. Who was he?

356 Who was the only English player in Liverpool's team in their first ever League match?

357 John Houlding, the man who founded Liverpool, was known by what nickname?

358 In 1892/93 Liverpool won two trophies which were stolen. Can you name them?

359 The team which failed in an election bid to senior football in 1893, the year Liverpool made it, were also a local side. Who were they?

360 What record did the Reds set when winning the 1894 second division championship?

361 Who did Liverpool beat in a Test Match for promotion to Division 1 in 1894?

362 Liverpool's first win in the first division came in their tenth attempt. Who did they beat?

363 Who were Liverpool's first-ever first division opponents?

364 Who was the first Liverpool player to score in the first division?

365 Who was the first Liverpool player to score in a Football League match?

366 What was the score in the first Merseyside derby?

367 The first time Liverpool beat Everton in the League they won 3-1. In which month of which year?

368 Who were Liverpool's first opponents in the FA Cup proper?

369 Who were the first team Liverpool played in League football?

370 Who were the first team to beat Liverpool in League football?

371 Liverpool had their biggest ever League win in 1896. What was the score, and who were the opposition?

Ian St John, a long-time Merseyside favourite.

372 In 1893 Liverpool met London opposition for the first time. Which team, and what was the score?

373 Forget it if you can't name this man on the right.

374 How many international caps did he win in his career?

375 For which Scottish Junior team did he once play?

376 Who was his first senior manager?

43

377 When Liverpool beat Ferencvaros 2-1 on aggregate in the 1970/71 Fairs Cup, who scored an away goal to ensure Liverpool's win?

378 What was the half-time score of the 1973 UEFA Cup final second leg against Borussia Munchengladbach?

379 In the 1974/75 Cup Winners Cup Liverpool beat Stromsgodset Drammen 11-0 at Anfield. Apart from Clemence, who was the only player who didn't get on the scoresheet?

380 In the 1975/76 UEFA Cup final against Bruges in the first leg, who came on as a substitute and scored?

381 When Bobby Graham made his European debut for Liverpool he was substituted. Name the opposition and the player who replaced him?

382 In the 1971/72 Cup Winners Cup second round who beat Liverpool 3-1 on aggregate?

383 Name the two East German teams Liverpool beat in the 1972/73 UEFA Cup?

384 In the 1973/74 European Cup Liverpool struggled to a 3-1 aggregate win in the first round against which team?

385 In the 1975/76 UEFA Cup second round what was the aggregate score against Real Sociedad?

386 When Liverpool won the 1977 European Cup who did they beat in the semis?

387 Who was the first substitute Liverpool used in a European tie?

388 In the 1975/76 UEFA Cup semi-final Liverpool beat Barcelona 2-1 on aggregate. Who were the Reds' two scoring heroes?

389 Who beat Liverpool in the semi-final of the 1970/71 Fairs Cup?

390 In the 1973/74 European Cup second round, which team beat Liverpool 2-1 both home and away?

391 Who beat Liverpool on away goals in the 1974/75 Cup Winners Cup?

392 Whose only European goal came in the quarter-final of the 1970/71 Fairs Cup against Bayern Munich in a 1-1 draw?

393 Against which team did Kevin Keegan make his European debut?

394 Liverpool beat Borussia Munchengladbach 3-0 in the first leg of the 1972/73 UEFA Cup final. Who were the scorers?

395 Where was the 1977 European Cup final played?

396 In the semi-final of the 1972/73 UEFA Cup Liverpool beat Spurs by virtue of an away goal. Who scored it?

WHERE DID THEY COME FROM (2)

397 From where did Liverpool sign 20's hero Dick Forshaw?

398 Name the club that Tom Bradshaw left to come to Anfield, and the then club record fee Liverpool paid for him?

399 Where did Laurie Hughes play League football as an amateur before coming to Liverpool?

400 What was the year and the fee when Alex Lindsay left Bury to join the Reds?

401 In 1962 Bill Shankly bought a player who was languishing in a Scottish reserve team at the time. Name the player and his previous club?

402 Name the year and the fee involved when Liverpool signed John Toshack from Cardiff?

Steve McMahon finds the net against his old team, Everton.

403 From where did Liverpool capture their great Scottish centre-half Alex Raisbeck?

404 From where did the Reds sign goalkeeper Cyril Sidlow?

405 How did Tom Bromilow arrive at Anfield after the First World War?

406 From which club, and in which year, did Liverpool sign young Gary Gillespie?

407 Name the club he left, and the fee Liverpool paid when Emlyn Hughes arrived at the club?

408 What fee did Liverpool pay Newcastle for Alan Kennedy?

409 Tommy Miller, the successful Scots centre-forward before and after the First World War, joined Liverpool from which club?

410 From which Scottish club did Liverpool sign Steve Nicol?

411 In which year did Graeme Souness leave Middlesbrough for Anfield?

412 What was Ronnie Whelan's Irish League side before he crossed the water to Liverpool?

413 Jimmy Harrower left his native Scotland in 1957 to come to Anfield, but with which Scottish club did he star?

414 Goalkeeper Kenny Campbell played for which Scottish club before joining Liverpool. Once a senior team, this club now plays in the Junior ranks over the Border?

415 Liverpool paid out big money for Mark Lawrenson. How big, and who got it?

416 Legendary keeper Sam Hardy played for a couple of seasons for which team before Liverpool snapped him up?

WHERE DID THEY GO? (2)

417 Name the twenties half-back who played 200 games for Liverpool before moving to Queens Park Rangers in 1928?

418 Which club received the services of Larry Lloyd when he left Anfield?

419 Where did Howard Gayle go when he finished with Liverpool?

420 Which team did Phil Boersma join in 1976?

421 In 1934 Elisha Scott became player/manager of which team in his native country?

422 When John McGregor signed for Liverpool, he spent time on loan to which two clubs?

423 In 1962 John Molyneux left Liverpool to rejoin his first senior club. Can you name it?

424 Which Spanish club did John Toshack manage?

425 What was the fee involved when Jimmy Case joined Brighton in 1981?

426 Where did Joey Jones go on leaving Liverpool?

427 Alun Evans went back to the Midlands after he left Anfield. Which club did he join?

428 Where did Alan A'Court move to when his time at Anfield came to an end?

429 When Tommy Miller lost his striker's position at Anfield in 1921, which team did he join?

Bob Paisley and Graeme Souness with a brace of prizes.

430 Dick White, the fifties defender, joined which team when he left Liverpool?

431 In 1970 where did Geoff Strong go when he finished playing for Liverpool?

432 In December 1985, Phil Neal became player/manager of which team?

433 After nine seasons at Anfield, Tom Bradshaw left the club in 1938 and returned to his native Scotland to play for which team?

434 In which year did Ray Clemence leave Liverpool for Spurs?

435 Can you name the year and the club he joined when Bobby Graham left Anfield?

436 For which club did Steve Heighway sign after his Liverpool days?

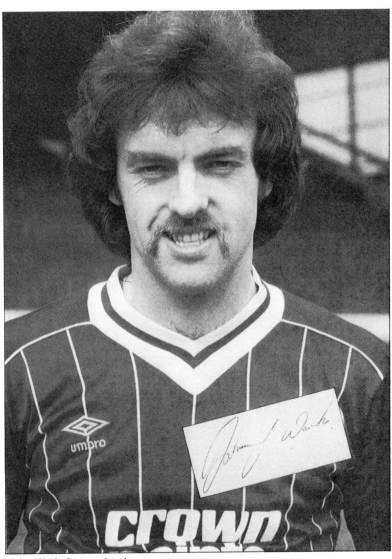

John Wark, Liverpool stalwart.

437 Do you recognise this player?

438 Where is he now player/manager?

439 With which Italian team did he play?

440 What winners medal did he pick up in his first season at Anfield?

Liverpool had just won the League championship for the second successive year. Manager David Ashworth had a team chock-full of personality and international players. See what you know about the season.

441 Who finished as top scorer in the League matches?

442 Who hit a hat-trick at Anfield in the first game of the season against Arsenal?

443 In the first round of the Cup, which team did Liverpool beat 4-1 away from home after a 0-0 draw at Anfield?

444 Who was the only man who played all games in both championship-winning teams of 1921/22 and 22/23?

445 Centre-half Walter Wadsworth played a major part in retaining the Championship. Where was he born?

446 Who did Liverpool beat 2-0 away from home in the second round of the FA Cup, thanks to goals from Johnson and Forshaw?

447 Apart from Elisha Scott and Dick Forshaw, who else played in all the League games of the season?

448 The heaviest defeat Liverpool suffered was 4-1. Who inflicted it?

449 Who won his only Scotland cap against Wales near the end of the season?

450 When Eph Longworth missed his only game of the season against Huddersfield, who took his place for *his* only game of the season?

451 Name the popular centre-forward who only managed one game that season because of the form of Dick Johnson?

452 To win the title, Liverpool took three out of four points in the last two games of the season against the same team. Which team?

453 Liverpool beat Everton 5-1 in a League match after being 0-1 down at half-time. Who scored a second-half hat-trick for Liverpool?

454 Bill Lacey's reserve played ten league games and scored once. Who was he?

455 Liverpool went out of the FA Cup in the third round at Anfield by 1-2 to which team?

456 What was the total crowd attracted to the two League games against Everton?

457 Which half-back scored only three League goals, but was known to be the playmaker of the team?

458 How many shut-outs did Elisha Scott achieve in 42 League games?

459 Fred Hopkin's first League goal in March 1923 coincided with which incident?

460 Which player finished second-top League scorer?

REDS IN THE FA CUP (3)
THE BUILDING YEARS

461 In 1953 Liverpool lost in the third round to a team stuggling in the third division north. Who were they?

462 In 1957 a team from the third division south took the Reds to the cleaners again. Who were this team?

463 In 1958 Southend took Liverpool to a replay before the Reds got through 3-2 with goals from three players all of whom hit their only Cup goal for Liverpool in that match. Can you name them?

464 By 1959 the Rabbits hoodoo hit catastrophic proportions as the Reds went out of the Cup to a non-League team. Who were they?

465 When Liverpool won the Cup for the first time in their history in 1965, which players got the two Cup final glory goals?

466 In the 1963 Cup, a Roger Hunt goal was enough for a sixth round win over which team?

467 In the 1968 Cup, all of Liverpool's four ties went to replays. Can you name the four teams involved?

468 Whose only Cup goal came in a third round tie in 1971 against Aldershot at Anfield which gave Liverpool a 1-0 win on their road to Wembley?

469 In 1963 Liverpool lost in the semi final. To which team, and where?

470 In 1971 who got the only goal of a sixth round replay with Spurs at White Hart Lane to give Reds a win with his first Cup goal?

471 In 1960 he scored in the first minute of his first Cup tie against Leyton Orient. Need we ask who?

472 Who did Liverpool beat in the 1965 semi-final and by what score?

473 Even in 1965 Liverpool had trouble with Rabbits and had to replay which team who grabbed a 1-1 draw at Anfield?

474 In the 1963 Cup, which team knocked Liverpool out at the third attempt?

475 In 1970, Liverpool lost in the sixth round to which second division team?

476 In 1964 which team beat Liverpool at Anfield by 2-1 in a sixth round tie?

477 How did 105,000 fans get to watch the 1967 fifth round tie with Everton, which Liverpool lost 0-1?

478 Who scored a last-minute penalty in extra time of a fourth round replay against Burnley in 1963?

479 Who did Liverpool beat in the 1965 quarter-finals after a drawn game?

480 After winning the 1965 Cup Liverpool went out at the first attempt the following year at Anfield. Who were the team who beat the Reds.?

THE LEAGUE CAMPAIGNS (3)

481 In 1895/96 Liverpool won promotion again. How many goals did they score in 15 home games?

482 He came into the team for the last few games of 1907/08, scored five goals and was top scorer the next season. Who?

483 In 1981/82 Terry McDermott was second-top League scorer with 14 goals. How many games did he play in?

484 Against which team did Steve McMahon make his League debut in 1985/86?

485 Who was top League scorer in 1979/80 with 21 goals?

486 On New Year's Day 1934 Liverpool lost 2-9. Where?

487 What's the lowest amount of games the Reds have won from a 42 game League programme?

488 During Liverpool's stay in the second division which team won it twice?

489 Who scored 15 goals in only 20 games in the 1964 Championship-winning team?

490 In 1974/75 Liverpool were second in the League. Who won it?

491 Name the Scot who broke into the team in season 1977/78 in a match against Derby?

492 What was the score when Liverpool beat Higher Walton in their first ever match in the Lancashire League?

493 Who took over as centre-half when Alex Raisbeck left Anfield?

494 Liverpool used 26 players when they won the 1947 League title. How many had played for the Reds before the war?

495 Liverpool used two right wingers in consecutive League matches in 1959 and for both it was their first and last game. Name them.

496 When the Reds won the title in 1966 using only 14 players, one man played in only the last game. Who was he?

Ronnie Whelan goes in against Gordon Strachan.

Jim Beglin sets up another hit.

497 When the Reds clinched the 1980 title at Anfield by beating Villa 4-1 who scored his only goal for the club in that match?

498 Who started only three League games in 1982/83 and scored three goals?

499 Who won the 1985 title when the Reds were second?

500 In 1899 Liverpool lost the title when they went down at Villa, but what was significant about the crowd in that match?

MISCELLANEOUS

501 In the 1975 Charity Shield who missed a penalty for Leeds United against Liverpool?

502 Which former Liverpool player appeared in all four divisions of the League in the space of a year?

503 Which man, formerly on the books of Liverpool, eventually became head of the PFA?

504 Who took over as club captain from Eph Longworth in 1914?

505 Where was Billy Liddell born?

506 Who was the first South African to play for Liverpool?

507 In which Welsh village was Ian Rush born?

508 Sam Raybould played for three teams before Liverpool. How many can you name?

509 Jimmy Payne played six games for which other team before retiring from football?

510 Before he came south to England, which Scottish club did Alex Raisbeck play for?

511 Where was Bob Paisley born?

512 What was the only jersey Matt McQueen did not wear in League matches for the Reds?

513 In December 1893 Liverpool beat Ardwick 3-0 in a second division match. Why was the team selection unique?

514 Name the man who was Press Steward at Anfield for 44 years?

515 In which year did Ronnie Moran join Liverpool?

516 In May 1947 Liverpool beat Wolves in the last match to win the League championship. Who was captain of Wolves then?

517 With which Scottish amateur team did John Wark play?

518 When Ian Rush won the Golden Boot in 1984 how many British players had won it before him?

519 Which former Liverpool player once won the famous Powderhall Professional Sprint race held annually in Scotland?

520 Who became club captain after Graeme Souness left Anfield?

The 1899-1900 Liverpool squad.

521 Who is this player?

522 In which year did he sign professional forms with Liverpool?

523 Against which team did he make his League debut?

524 What was the first Cup final he played in?

Liverpool became the champions of Europe and the champions of England in the same season, a culmination of the efforts of many years of building. They also just missed out on the FA Cup, losing out in the final. What do you remember about this glorious season?

525 Which team finished second in the League to Liverpool?

526 Who did Liverpool beat in a replay in the FA Cup semi-final?

527 The Reds went out of the League Cup at the first hurdle to which team by 0-1 after a 1-1 draw?

528 Ian Callaghan and Terry McDermott scored only one League goal each, and they came in the same game. Who were the opposition?

529 Who did the Reds beat 7-0 on aggregate in the first round of the European Cup?

530 Who beat Liverpool in the FA Cup final?

531 Who scored Borussia Munchengladbach's goal in the European Cup final?

532 Name the two ever presents in the League-winning side apart from Ray Clemence?

533 He had been at Liverpool for a couple of years, but the first League game of the season was his League debut. Who?

534 What was the aggregate score against FC Zurich in the semi-finals of the European Cup?

535 Ray Kennedy had made the number 5 jersey his own, but who wore it when he missed his only League game against Derby?

536 Which third division team took the Reds to an FA Cup third round replay?

537 When Liverpool beat Everton 3-1 in the League match at Anfield, what was the half-time score?

538 Who scored Liverpool's FA Cup final goal?

539 His first Cup goal for Liverpool came in the sixth round win over Middlesbrough at Anfield. Who?

540 Keegan scored his last goal at Anfield during the season against which team?

541 They were the first team to hit five against Liverpool in a League match for nearly 15 years and they did it all in the first half. Who?

542 His only League game, the last of the season against Bristol City, was his last game in a Liverpool jersey. Who was he?

543 He started only one FA Cup match before the final but played in the final, so can you name him?

544 Name the team which won the European Cup?

REDS IN EUROPE (4)

545 Who beat Liverpool on away goals in the 1969/70 Fairs Cup?

Kevin Keegan, using the head against Ipswich.

546 When Liverpool won the 1977 European Cup who did they beat in the third round?

547 In the 1975/76 UEFA Cup, when Liverpool beat Real Sociedad 6-1, a player made his European debut which turned out to be his only European tie. He was substituted by another player making his only European appearance. Name them both?

548 Who were the first team to score against Ray Clemence in a European tie?

549 Which Scottish team did Liverpool beat in the third round of the 1970/71 Fairs Cup?

550 When Liverpool lost 2-4 on aggregate to Red Star Belgrade in the 1973/74 European Cup, which Reds player scored both home and away?

551 In the 1976 UEFA Cup final second leg against Bruges, who scored Liverpool's goal in the 1-1 draw?

552 In the 1980/81 European Cup second round which Scottish internationalist scored an own goal at Anfield?

553 In the 1976/77 European Cup against FC Zurich in the semi-final second leg at Anfield, who came on as a substitute for Steve Heighway for his only European appearance?

554 In the 1981 European Cup semi-final against Bayern Munich, who scored an away goal in the 1-1 draw in Germany?

555 In 1981/82 Liverpool beat Oulu Palloseura yet again. What was the aggregate score?

556 Who scored Liverpool's goal in the 1984 European Cup final?

557 Who were Liverpool's three scorers in the 1977 European Cup final?

558 Who did Liverpool beat in the 1978 European Cup semi-finals?

559 In the 1982/83 European Cup second round Liverpool lost the first leg by 1-0 and won the second 5-0. Who were the opposition?

560 Who scored Munchengladbach's goal in the 1977 European Cup final?

561 Against which team did Ian Rush score his first European goal?

562 Who did Liverpool beat in the semi-finals of the 1984 European Cup?

Supersub David Fairclough — as usual looking for the net.

563 In the 1977/78 European Cup first round first leg at Anfield, Liverpool beat Dinamo Dresden 5-1. Who got a double for the Reds in that match?

564 Who put Liverpool out of the 1979/80 European Cup in the first round?

INTERNATIONAL REDS (2)

565 Name the defender who won three of his four England caps while with Liverpool in 1970/71?

566 Name the three Liverpool players who played together for Eire in 1985?

567 Alec Lindsay won his first England cap in a friendly 2-2 draw at Wembley against which famous footballing country?

568 What record did Elisha Scott set for his country in 1929 that stood until 1976?

569 Against which country did Gordon Milne make his England debut in 1963 at Wembley?

570 Who was Ireland's keeper before Elisha Scott took over in 1920?

571 Name the two Liverpool players who took part in the 1986 World Cup?

572 In a memorable 5-0 Wales victory at Wrexham in 1983 Ian Rush hit a double before going off. Who were Wales hammering?

573 Apart from Roger Hunt which other Liverpool player took part in the 1966 World Cup?

574 When Kevin Keegan got his first England goal in Cardiff against Wales in a 2-0 win, name the other England winger who scored his only international goal in that match.

575 Against which country did Kenny Dalglish win his 100th Scottish cap?

576 He played centre-half for Scotland in two games in 1931 which Scotland lost 0-5 and 0-3 and was never picked again. Who was he?

577 David Johnson got two goals for England in his second game as England won 3-1 at Wembley in 1980. Who were the opposition?

578 Against which country did Roger Hunt score on his England debut?

579 Kenny Dalglish won more than half his Scotland caps while with Liverpool. True or false?

580 Against whom did Ray Clemence win his last England cap as a Liverpool player?

581 In a 0-0 draw with Switzerland at Wembley in 1977 Liverpool supplied seven of the England team. Can you name them?

582 In the 1982 World Cup match against Kuwait in Bilbao, who partnered Phil Thomson at the heart of the England defence?

583 Apart from Alex Raisbeck, which other Liverpool defender was capped for Scotland against England in 1906?

584 In 1965 Ian St John scored in his last game for Scotland in a famous 2-2 draw against which country?

585 Who is this player?

586 By what nickname was he known at Anfield?

587 From which team did Liverpool sign him?

588 Where was he once player/manager?

589 Liverpool won the League for the first time in 1900/01, but there were two teams they couldn't beat. Can you name them?

590 In the 1969/70 League campaign Liverpool had five players whose surnames began with the letter 'L'. Can you name them?

591 In 1978/79 Liverpool won their first six League games. Which famous team did they beat 7-0 in one of those games?

592 As panic set in in 1953/54, how many players did the Reds go through in their battle to stay in the top League?

593 Why did the date 1/12/59 change the history of the club?

594 In February 1964 Ian St John hit his first League hat-trick for the Reds at Anfield in a 6-1 win against which team?

595 In 1977/78 who was second-top League scorer behind Kenny Dalglish?

596 Who scored on his League debut for Liverpool in the first 12 minutes of the first League match of the 1971/72 season?

597 Who became the second player in the history of the club to hit five in a League match in 1954 against Bristol City?

598 In 1962/63 Liverpool returned to the first division, but where did they finish?

599 How many of the team that played in the last game of the 1961/62 season in the second division played in the first game of the first division campaign the following season?

600 In 1895/96 in his first year at Anfield he scored 25 goals in 20 games. Who was he?

601 In 1893/94, Liverpool's first season in the Football League, which player was their only ever-present?

602 In January 1981 who became the first team to beat the Reds in the League at Anfield for three years?

603 In which season did Liverpool win the League title for the second time?

604 Gordon Milne's last League game was in 1967 as the Reds went down 1-3 to Blackpool. Milne was substituted in that game by which player?

605 How many times was Billy Liddell top League scorer for Liverpool?

606 Who were promoted with Liverpool in 1961/62?

607 As Kenny Dalglish burst on to the scene in 1977 how many goals did he score in his first six League matches?

608 In 1984/85 John Wark hit a League hat-trick away to which team?

This was the season Liverpool proved themselves an international class team by winning the UEFA Cup, their first European trophy. By the way, they also sewed up the small matter of another First Division championship. Let's see what you remember about this star-studded side.

609 What was remarkable about John Toshack finishing top League scorer with Kevin Keegan?

Sammy Lee in the wars with Paul Breitner.

69

610 Who did Liverpool beat 2-0 on aggregate in the UEFA Cup first round?

611 How many seasons had Liverpool gone without winning a major trophy?

612 Who scored Liverpool's goal in the fifth round of the League Cup in a 1-1 draw with Spurs to earn the Reds a replay?

613 Ray Clemence missed his only League game between 1971 and 1978 against Derby. Who took his place to play his only League match for the Reds?

614 Liverpool won the UEFA Cup, but who scored the first goal of their campaign?

615 How many of Liverpool's FA Cup and League Cup ties went to a replay?

616 Which player was substituted in both legs of the UEFA Cup final?

617 Who put Liverpool out of the FA Cup in the fourth round?

618 In his first league game at Anfield he scored in a 4-2 win over Wolves. Who was the player?

619 Which second division team took the Reds to a replay in the second round of the League Cup?

620 In the second round of the UEFA Cup Liverpool beat AEK Athens 3-1 in Greece. Who scored the goals?

621 Which youngster, not long in the team wore the number 9 jersey in the last League game of the season against Leicester at Anfield?

622 Who scored in the dying seconds of extra time in the replayed third round of the League Cup to give Liverpool a win over West Brom?

623 He was joint top scorer in the UEFA Cup with Keegan yet he only appeared as a substitute in the second leg of the final. Who was he?

624 Who were the only team to win at Anfield in the League in this season?

625 Which second division team took the Reds to a replay in the third round of the FA Cup?

626 Who put Liverpool out of the League Cup?

627 This man played more Cup ties than League games during the season, and left Anfield the following year. Who?

628 Who did Liverpool beat in the fourth round of the League
Cup?

629 Identify this former Anfield star?

630 How much did he cost Liverpool?

631 Against which team did he make his first team debut?

632 How many European Cup finals did he play in?

633 What was significant about the 1984 European Cup final against Roma?

634 In the 1980/81 European Cup who did the Reds beat 5-0 on aggregate in the second round?

635 Who played and scored in the first two rounds of the 1977 European Cup but did not play in the final?

636 Against which team did Kenny Dalglish score his first European goal for Liverpool?

637 Who scored Liverpool's goal in the 1981 European Cup final?

638 In round two of the 1983/84 European Cup Liverpool beat Bilbao 1-0 in Spain for a 1-0 aggregate win. Who scored the goal?

639 Who did Liverpool beat 4-1 away from home in the third round of the 1983/84 European Cup?

640 Against which team did Graeme Souness make his European debut for Liverpool?

641 Name the two teams who beat Liverpool on their way to winning the 1977 European Cup?

642 In round three of the 1981 European Cup who scored a hat-trick at Anfield against CSKA Sofia?

643 When Liverpool lost 1-2 on aggregate to CSKA Sofia in the 1982 European Cup, who scored in the 1-0 win at Anfield for Liverpool?

644 Name the two players who made their European debuts for Liverpool in the 1977/78 European Cup against Dinamo Dresden at Anfield?

645 In the 1981/82 European Cup Liverpool scraped through the second round on a 5-4 aggregate against which side?

646 Against which team did Steve Nicol make his European debut?

647 Who scored Liverpool's goal in the 1978 European Cup final?

648 What was the aggregate score when Liverpool beat CSKA Sofia in the 1981 European Cup third round?

649 Who put Liverpool out of the 1982/83 European Cup on a 3-4 aggregate?

650 Who beat Liverpool in the first round of the 1978/79 European Cup, and what was the aggregate score?

651 Where was the 1981 European Cup final against Real Madrid played?

652 Against which team did Ian Rush make his Liverpool debut?

After eight long years languishing in the wilderness of the second division, Liverpool won that League to secure their return to their rightful place. It was a milestone in the history of the club, so let's see what you know about it.

653 The Reds set a new club record for League goals scored — how many did they notch up?

654 Which first division team did Liverpool beat in the FA Cup third round?

655 Which young player had one League outing as a replacement for Ian St John?

656 Who took over the keeper's job from Bert Slater late in the season?

657 Name the four players who appeared in every League game?

658 Roger Hunt set a new club record for League goals in a season. How many did he hit?

659 Liverpool did not lose in the League until their twelfth match. Which club ended the run?

660 Not noted for goals, he got one to earn a 3-3 draw with Orient to maintain Liverpool's unbeaten home record. Who?

661 At Preston in his first game of the season he scored his only goal of the season. Who?

662 Who got four of Liverpool's six FA Cup goals?

663 Roger Hunt's scoring feats were rewarded by his first England cap. He scored again. Who were England playing?

664 He scored the first goal of the League campaign, but later lost his place to Ian Callaghan. Who was he?

665 Roger Hunt hit five League hat-tricks. Name the teams on the wrong end.

666 Which other Scot, apart from St John, played his first full season in a Liverpool jersey?

667 In a League match against Plymouth at Anfield, which stalwart made his farewell appearance for Liverpool?

668 Liverpool beat them twice in the League but lost to them in the FA Cup after three ties. Which team was this?

669 At which ground did Liverpool go out of the FA Cup?

670 After the celebrations, Liverpool lost their last League game. Who spoiled the party?

671 Ian St John got in on Roger Hunt's hat-trick act against which team?

672 Why was St John's move to Anfield at the start of the season surprising?

REDS IN THE FA CUP (4)
THE SEVENTIES

673 In the 1971 Cup final Liverpool lost 2-1 to Arsenal. Who scored for the Reds?

674 When the Reds won the FA Cup in 1974 who did they beat in the final?

675 In 1977 who did Liverpool beat 2-0 in the quarter-finals?

676 In the 1974 semi-finals it took two games to overcome Leicester. Where were they played?

677 In the third round of the 1979 Cup an old team came back to haunt Liverpool and took them to a replay. Who?

678 In 1978 he scored his first Cup goal for Liverpool but the Reds lost 2-4 to Chelsea. Who?

679 In the 1971 Cup final who played as a substitute for Alun Evans?

680 In 1971 the Reds beat Everton 2-1 in the semi-final. Name Liverpool's two scorers.

681 Which team took Liverpool to a fourth round replay in 1974 which the Reds won 2-0 after a 0-0 draw at Anfield?

682 In 1975 Liverpool lost in the fourth round to which team?

683 In the 2-4 defeat by Chelsea in 1978 who scored Liverpool's first goal?

684 Who scored his first Cup goal for Liverpool in a fifth round tie against Burnley in 1979?

685 Kevin Keegan opened his Cup scoring account with Liverpool with a double against which team in 1972 in the third round?

686 In 1974 Liverpool beat Bristol City 1-0 in the sixth round. Who scored the goal?

687 In 1979 who beat Liverpool 1-0 at Goodison in a replayed semi-final?

688 Who put Liverpool out of the 1976 FA Cup in the fourth round?

689 Who made his Cup debut for the Reds as a substitute for Joey Jones in a third round tie in 1978 against Chelsea?

690 When Liverpool lost the 1977 Cup final to Manchester United who came on as a substitute for David Johnson?

691 The successful 1974 Cup campaign got off to a bad start with a 2-2 draw at Anfield against which team?

692 Who scored his first Cup goal for Liverpool in the 1977 semi-final against Everton which ended in a 2-2 draw?

INTERNATIONAL REDS (3)

693 Which Liverpool player played for England against the Rest of the World at Wembley in 1963?

694 Emlyn Hughes scored only once in 62 England outings. Who was the unlucky goalkeeper he scored against?

695 Against which country did Kenny Dalglish score his last Scotland goal?

696 In 1949 when Scotland beat Wales 2-0 in Glasgow what was unusual about Billy Liddell's appearance in the game?

697 In 1986 Ian Rush became the first Liverpool player to line up against which country?

698 Who was the first Liverpool player to score for Scotland?

699 Apart from Emlyn Hughes, who has been capped most times for England while a Liverpool player?

700 Emlyn Hughes won his first England cap in 1969. Where?

701 Who was the first Liverpool player capped for Wales?

702 How many Liverpool players have scored for Northern Ireland?

703 When David Johnson won his first England cap in 1980 against Eire at Wembley he was substituted. Who came on in his place?

704 Who was the last Liverpool defender capped for England?

705 Name three Liverpool keepers who have been capped for Scotland?

706 Ian Rush made his Wales debut in which famous stadium?

707 In 1961 he scored a double in two consecutive games for Scotland. Who?

708 Who was the first Liverpool player to score for England?

709 Who scored on his England debut against Wales in 1976 in Wrexham?

710 Who was the only Liverpool player in the England team which lost to the USA in the 1950 World Cup finals in Brazil?

711 There were three years, 1963-1966, between this Liverpool defender's only two England caps. Who?

712 Roger Hunt scored three goals in the 1966 World Cup. Against which two countries did the goals come?

Jack Balmer, a Liverpool hero of the past.

713 Do you recognise this old Anfield favourite?

714 With which country was he an internationalist before England?

715 He scored a record goals total in 1931. How many in the season?

716 At what other sport did he reach professional standard?

717 Which trophy did Independiente win to qualify to play Liverpool in the World Cup Championship in Tokyo?

718 Kevin MacDonald's first team play in the Scottish Highland League. Can you name them?

719 Who sold Kevin MacDonald to Liverpool?

720 Name the 17-year-old striker Liverpool signed from Oldham in 1984?

721 When Liverpool beat Newcastle in the 1974 FA Cup final, who was manager of Newcastle?

722 Which former Liverpool player once managed Stoke for a short period?

723 Whose nickname at Anfield was Barney Rubble?

724 Who did Liverpool play in Alan Hansen's 500th senior match?

725 When Aston Villa won the 1982 European Cup their captain was Liverpool-born. Who was he?

726 To which prestige job was club chairman John Smith appointed in 1985?

727 When was John Smith made chairman of Liverpool?

728 In the 1974 FA Cup final who was the youngest player in the Newcastle team?

729 Who played in the first Cup final held at Wembley then went on to manage Liverpool?

730 Which club did Peter Wall join when he left Liverpool in 1970?

731 Sam Hardy won two FA Cup winners medals with which club?

732 Ray Clemence had stiff opposition in his 700th senior appearance. The match was at Anfield. Who were the team?

733 In Bruce Grobbelaar's reserve debut the little Reds won 2-0 where?

734 Who left Liverpool for Swansea in 1981 and was immediately made captain of that club?

735 What was special about Bruce Grobbelaar's last match for Crewe?

736 What was Mark Lawrenson's first senior club?

737 Liverpool had to replay their first ever Cup tie at Luton after a 1-1 draw at Anfield. What was the result in the replay?

738 In the 1968/69 Cup who did Liverpool beat 4-0 in the second round?

739 Who put the Reds out of the 1976/77 Cup after a replay at the first hurdle?

740 In the 1977/78 semi-final first leg Liverpool beat Arsenal 2-1 at Anfield. Name the players who got the Reds' goals.

741 Who beat Liverpool in the 1978/79 Cup at the first attempt?

742 In 1969/70 Liverpool went out 2-3 in the third round to which team?

743 In the fifth round in 1979/80 Liverpool beat which team 3-1 away from home with David Johnson (2) and Kenny Dalglish scoring?

744 In the 1972/73 Cup every Reds match went to a replay. Name the four teams involved.

745 In the third round of the 1977/78 Cup Liverpool beat Derby 2-0. Who came on as a substitute and scored both goals in the space of three minutes?

746 In the 1978 final Liverpool lost 0-1 to Nottingham Forest. Who scored that crucial goal?

The squad for season 1981-82.

747 In the 1986 semi-final against QPR which players got the goals for Liverpool in the 2-2 draw at Anfield?

748 In the 1982/83 Cup who did Liverpool beat 3-1 on aggregate in the semi-final?

749 In the fifth round of 1981/82 Liverpool were held to a 0-0 draw at Anfield before winning the replay 3-1. Who were they playing?

750 In 1983/84 the Reds were taken to a second replay which they won with a Souness goal in extra time. Who were the opposition?

751 Where was the 1981 final replay with West Ham played?

752 In the 1980 semi-final the Reds drew 1-1 with Forest. Who scored in the last minute for Liverpool?

753 In 1977/78 Kenny Dalglish scored in his first League Cup match as Liverpool beat which team 2-0?

754 Who put the Reds out of the 1974/75 Cup at Anfield?

755 In 1968/69 Liverpool lost in round four to Arsenal by 1-2. Who got the Reds' consolation goal?

756 In 1967/68 who beat Liverpool 2-3 in a replay in the second round?

THE LEAGUE CAMPAIGNS (5)

757 Liverpool lost a Test Match in 1895 to stay in the first division. Who beat them?

758 In 1893 against Walsall Swifts a player scored Liverpool's first League hat-trick. Who was he?

759 In 1899 Liverpool lost the League title in the last game to Aston Villa. What was the score?

760 Liverpool lost eight goals twice in ten weeks at the start of season 1934/35. Who were the two opponents involved?

761 Between 1930-1939 what was the Reds' highest League finish?

762 What record was created when Liverpool drew 1-1 with Everton at Goodison in September 1948?

763 In 1968/69 Liverpool were runners-up in the League to which team?

764 Who was top League scorer for the Reds in 1969/70 season?

765 In the first League game Ray Clemence played in 1970, Liverpool lost 0-1 to which team?

766 David Fairclough earned the nickname 'Supersub', but how many goals did he score as a substitute in League matches?

767 In 1980/81 Terry McDermott was top League scorer with how many goals?

768 In 1982 Liverpool won the League but their last game was a 0-0 draw away to which team?

769 When the Reds won the first division for the first time in 1901, who was their top scorer with 16 goals?

770 In that same team who was the goalkeeper who was unbeaten in the last four matches?

771 The year after they first won the championship, in what position did Liverpool finish?

Bob Paisley — Manager of the Century.

772 In 1953-54 Liverpool lost five goals in three consecutive League matches, all away from home. Which three teams did the damage?

773 In 1955/56, 56/57 59/60 and 60/61, Liverpool finished in the same position in the second division. What position?

774 Liverpool won the 1962 second division title but said farewell to a full back who had given the club seven years solid service. Who was he?

775 In 1982/83 Terry McDermott played his last League game for Liverpool as a substitute away to which team?

776 Who played for six seasons, wasn't in the team at all in 1981/82 then came back to play a handful of games in 1982-83?

THE BACKROOM BOYS (2)

777 Who signed South African players Gordon Hodgson and Arthur Riley for Liverpool?

778 Up to the present, how many managers have Liverpool had?

779 Where was Bill Shankly born?

780 How many seasons did Liverpool have under the management of Bob Paisley?

781 Name two non-League teams Joe Fagan played for.

782 Who was Kenny Dalglish's first major signing for Liverpool?

783 Who was manager of the team that won the two successive League titles in 1921/22 and 22/23?

784 Who took the Reds to their first FA Cup final?

785 Name three other teams managed by David Ashworth.

786 What club did George Kaye manage before Liverpool?

787 Who was manager when tiny Worcester knocked the Reds out of the FA Cup?

788 On which date did Bill Shankly take over the reins at Anfield?

789 Name the two Football League teams Joe Fagan played for.

790 Who was the manager John McKenna sent to get Alex Raisbeck to Anfield?

791 Who signed Matt Busby for the Reds?

792 Which manager was in charge when Liverpool dropped into the second division in 1954?

793 Who brought Bob Paisley to Liverpool as a player?

794 Under which manager did Gordon Milne make his Liverpool debut?

795 The last signing Phil Taylor made for Liverpool was a player from Everton. Who was he?

796 Who became manager of Liverpool after Tom Watson?

797 Who is this former Liverpool hero?

798 In which year did he join Liverpool?

799 How many England caps did he win?

800 What team did he join on leaving Anfield?

801 Later a well-known manager he played his only League game for Liverpool in 1955 against Port Vale. Who?

802 He made his League debut four days after Bob Paisley and finished joint top scorer in 1946/47. Who?

803 Chris Lawler's League debut was a 2-2 draw in 1963 at Anfield against which team?

804 Bert Slater's last League game for Liverpool was at Anfield in 1962 and the Reds won 5-1. Who were they playing?

805 Who made his last League appearance in goal against Bolton in 1899?

806 Where did Emlyn Hughes make his League debut and what shirt did he wear?

807 In 1964/65 keeper Bill Molyneux played his one and only game for the Reds in a League match, the last of the season, against which team?

808 The last game of the 1909 season was Alex Raisbeck's last for Liverpool. It was against Newcastle, but what position did he play?

809 Billy Liddell's last League game was at Anfield against which team?

810 Liverpool lost 2-3 away to which team in Ronnie Moran's League debut in 1952?

811 In Bill Shankly's first League match in charge Liverpool beat which team 3-1 at Anfield?

812 Where did Elisha Scott make his League debut on New Year's Day 1913 as a replacement for Kenneth Campbell?

813 Tommy Lawrence, Chris Lawler and Billy Stevenson all made their League debut in 1962/63. Who was the first to do so?

814 Bob Paisley made his debut in a famous 7-4 win over which team?

815 Elisha Scott's last League game for Liverpool in 1934 was a 0-2 defeat in London against which side?

816 In 1906/07, Sam Hardy's first as Liverpool's goalkeeper, where did Liverpool finish in the League?

817 Who made his league debut for Liverpool in Billy Liddell's last game?

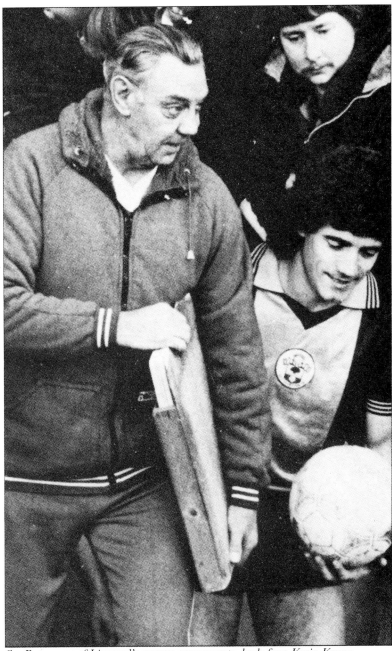

Joe Fagan, one of Liverpool's greatest ever servants, leads from Kevin Keegan.

818 Who did Liverpool beat 4-0 on Ian Callaghan's League debut in 1960?

819 Who made his League debut in the same game as Bob Paisley but could not claim a regular place in goal for five years?

820 He made his League debut at right-half in 1936 at Huddersfield and played in only two winning sides in his first 11 games. Who?

REDS IN EUROPE (6)
UP TO DATE

821 In 1985 his only 3 European ties were the European Cup semi finals and the final. Who?

822 Who did the Reds beat in the 1985 European Cup semi-finals?

823 In the 1984 European Cup final against Roma, who took the first of the penalty deciders for Liverpool and missed?

824 Who was the last Liverpool player to score on his European debut?

825 In the 1985 European Cup final who played in only his third European tie when he came on for Mark Lawrenson as a substitute?

826 Who scored Liverpool's opening goal in the 1984/85 European Cup tournament?

827 Where did Chris Lawler make his last European appearance for Liverpool?

828 In the 1977 Super Cup against Hamburg, who hit a hat-trick at Anfield as the Reds routed the Germans 6-0?

829 Who were the players who scored the deciding penalty kicks in the 1984 European Cup final?

830 Against which team did Emlyn Hughes make his last European appearance?

831 When Liverpool beat Benfica in the second round of the 1984/85 European Cup, what was the second leg score in Portugal?

832 What was unusual about Howard Gayle's only European appearance for Liverpool in 1981?

833 Who hit a first round hat-trick against Lech Poznan in the 1984/85 European Cup?

834 Who beat Liverpool 4-3 on aggregate in the 1978 Super Cup?

835 Who hit Benfica for three in the second round of the 1984/85 European Cup at Anfield?

836 How many European goals did Roger Hunt score for the Reds?

837 In the 1985 European Cup semi-final Liverpool beat Panathanaikos by 1-0 in Greece in the second leg. Who scored the Reds' goal?

838 Apart from Terry McDermott, which other Liverpool player scored three times in the Super Cup matches?

839 Who did Liverpool beat 5-2 on aggregate in round three of the 1984/85 European Cup?

840 What was the score in the 1985 Super Cup final against Juventus?

Another goal to celebrate from the Liverpool greats.

841 Name the year and the club he left when Avi Cohen joined Liverpool.

842 From which club did Liverpool secure the services of Joey Jones?

843 Before the turn of the century, Liverpool splashed out for flying winger Jack Cox. What club did he come from?

844 Joe Hewitt, at Anfield for over 40 years, started his professional career with which team?

845 From where did Liverpool sign Northern Ireland centre-forward Sam English?

846 Liverpool signed him as a raw centre-half after he had played only 28 first-team games for his Scottish club in the fifties. Name the player and the club he left for Liverpool?

847 Can you name the club he left and the fee paid for Larry Lloyd?

848 He signed in 1914 from Blackpool and scored 26 goals before the war started. Who was he?

849 Geoff Strong was a sixties stalwart at Anfield, but which team did he come from?

850 From which team did Liverpool sign Geoff Twentyman?

851 Nice and easy here. Where did Ray Clemence come from?

852 From which club did Liverpool capture left winger Fred Hopkin in the twenties?

853 Name the club he left, the year and the fee involved when a young Alun Evans came to Anfield?

854 John McKenna brought two brothers to Anfield from Scottish team Clyde before the turn of the century. Can you name them?

855 Twenties captain and full back Jimmy Jackson came from which club?

856 Born in Bootle, he played for Tranmere before joining the Reds from Bolton in 1956. Name the player.

857 Joe McQue, Liverpool's first League centre-half, led the Scottish contingent brought to Anfield by John McKenna. Where did he come from?

858 In May 1961 Liverpool paid a club record £35,000 for which Scottish player, and what team did he come from?

859 What team did the popular Albert Stubbins leave for Liverpool?

860 In 1960 Bill Shankly paid Preston £16,000 for a right-half. Who was he?

WHERE DID THEY GO (3)

861 In 1954 Kevin Baron left Liverpool to join one of the seaside clubs. Which one did he join?

862 Where did Alec Lindsay go after his years of sterling service at Anfield?

863 When Alan Kennedy left the club in 1985, which team did he go to?

864 With which continental club did David Fairclough have a spell when he left Liverpool?

865 Ian Callaghan was given a free transfer after his many glorious years at Anfield. Who did he join?

866 When the tricky but wayward Jimmy Payne left Liverpool in 1956, which team did he go to?

867 What was Tommy Smith's only other senior club apart from the Reds?

868 Phil Thomson crossed to Yorkshire when he left Liverpool. Where did he go to?

869 When Tommy Younger's Anfield career came to an end he returned to Scotland as player/manager of which team?

870 After over 400 games for Liverpool in 13 years up to the First World War, he left Anfield to play for Cardiff City. Who was he?

871 Peter Cormack was always a favourite at Anfield. Which club did he join after leaving the Reds?

872 Name the team he went to and the fee involved when Tony Hateley took his shooting boots elsewhere.

873 Ray Kennedy brought a fee of £160,000 to Anfield. Who paid it for the player's services?

874 Gordon Hodgson, Liverpool's second-highest scorer of all time, left Liverpool for which team in 1935?

875 Billy Lacey was a favourite winger at Anfield around the years of the First World War. Where did he finish his career?

876 When Alex Raisbeck left Liverpool he went back to Scotland

and played for two teams, finishing as manager and director of one. Can you name the two teams?

877 Where did Tony Rowley go when he left Liverpool in 1958?

878 When Peter Thompson left the Reds, which club did he join?

879 Where did popular twenties defender Walter Wadsworth finish up when he left Anfield?

880 One of Liverpool's most prolific scorers ever, Harry Chambers left the club in 1928 to go to which team?

REMEMBER THIS SEASON 1946/47

It was the first full season after the war, and teams had still a lot of rebuilding to do. Liverpool were fortunate that many of their players who had left off in 1939 were still at the club, but it was still a great achievement to win the first League title of a new era. See what you know about the season.

881 Who were the only team to beat Liverpool home and away in the League?

882 During the season Jack Balmer became the first player in history to hit hat-tricks in three consecutive League matches. Name the teams on the receiving end?

883 Who made his League debut in the third game of the season when Liverpool beat Chelsea 7-4?

884 Which player made a scoring debut late in the season against Aston Villa?

885 Liverpool had a great run-in in which they lost only one of their last 16 League games. Who beat them?

886 The Reds reached the FA Cup semi-final against Burnley, which went to a replay. Where was the first game played?

887 He only played in two League games, but scored the opening goal of the campaign to give the Reds a 1-0 win over Sheffield United. Who was he?

888 In November/December 1946 Jack Balmer scored in how many consecutive League games?

889 Against which team did Billy Liddell score his first League goal for Liverpool, and went on to make it a pair?

890 Who became Liverpool's regular keeper during the season?

891 Not noted for scoring, his only League goal of the season forced a crucial 1-1 draw with Derby County. Who was he?

892 In the FA Cup quarter-final Albert Stubbins hit a hat-trick against which team?

893 Who finished joint top League scorers for the season?

894 Veteran Berry Nieuwenhuys played half the season at outside-right. Who played the rest of the season in that position?

895 A Jack Balmer goal got the Reds through a tough FA Cup fifth round tie against which side?

896 Name the three goalkeepers Liverpool used in the League campaign?

897 Who was club captain during the season?

898 Where did Liverpool lose to Burnley in the FA Cup semi-final replay?

899 Who played his only League game for Liverpool against Blackpool?

900 Against which team did Jack Balmer hit four goals away from home?

REDS IN THE FA CUP (5)
THE EIGHTIES

901 Who scored Liverpool's goals in the 1986 Cup final against Everton?

902 In 1981 the Reds lost 2-1 to Everton in round four. Who scored for Liverpool in that match?

903 In the 1986 Cup who played in the third round and didn't play in the Cup again until the final?

904 In 1983 who shocked Liverpool 1-2 at Anfield in the fifth round?

905 Who scored Liverpool's goal in that game?

906 In 1980 who got a third round hat-trick against Grimsby at Anfield?

907 In 1986 who did Liverpool beat 5-0 in the third round?

908 In 1982 Ian Rush got a double in his first cup-tie. It was the third round. But who were the opposition?

909 Which non-League team scored at Anfield in a 1981 third round tie?

910 In 1985 when Liverpool lost 1-2 in a replayed semi-final to Manchester United, who scored Liverpool's goal?

911 In 1986 which player made five Cup appearances but did not play in the final?

912 Who took Liverpool to a shock fifth round replay in 1985?

913 In 1980 who did Liverpool beat away from home by 1-0 in the quarter-finals, and who scored the goal?

914 An Ian Rush double in the 1986 semi-final put Liverpool into the final. Who were the opposition and where was the game played?

915 In 1985 Liverpool had a 7-0 Cup victory. Who got a hat-trick in that game at Anfield?

916 The marathon 1980 semi-final against Arsenal went to four matches at three different venues. Name the venues?

917 The first semi-final against Manchester United in 1985 finished 2-2 after extra time. Name Liverpool's two scorers?

918 In the 1985 quarter-finals, an Ian Rush hat-trick helped the Reds to a 4-0 victory over which team?

919 In 1986 which team took Liverpool to a fifth round replay which the Reds only won 3-1 after extra time?

920 The first match of that fifth round tie finished 1-1. Who scored Liverpool's goal?

INTERNATIONAL REDS (4)

921 Who was the first player to score against Ray Clemence in an international match?

922 What was unusual about Peter Thompson's first six England caps?

923 In three appearances for Scotland Tommy Lawrence was on the winning side only once and still lost three goals. Against which country?

924 Billy Liddell's last goal for Scotland was on the continent. Who were Scotland playing?

925 In 1964 Roger Hunt hit four for England. Where?

926 Who was the first Liverpool player to score for Wales?

927 Sammy Lee scored on his England debut in which country?

928 England played a record 15 internationals in 1982. Which Liverpool player appeared in 11 of them?

929 Who was the first Liverpool player capped for England on foreign soil?

930 Two of Terry McDermott's three goals for England came in the same match at Wembley in 1980. Who were the opposition?

931 Phil Thompson scored only once for England, but in which unlikely place did that goal come?

932 Gordon Milne played for England against Northern Ireland at Wembley in 1963 when England won 8-3. What was special about that game?

933 Tommy Miller scored a double for Scotland in his only appearance for his country as a Liverpool player. Scotland lost 5-4 to which country, and where was the game played?

934 When Scotland lost 3-0 to Italy in 1965 in a World Cup qualifier, what jersey did Ron Yeats wear?

935 Who was the first Liverpool player capped for Wales against a foreign team?

936 Who was the first Liverpool player capped for Ireland?

937 Phil Taylor was capped only once against a foreign country. Which country was it?

938 Who played centre half for England in two games before the 1950 World Cup then lost his place in the team to clubmate Laurie Hughes?

939 Steve Nicol gained his first Scotland cap in a famous 6-1 win over which country at Hampden in 1984?

940 Roger Hunt's last England goal was at Wembley in 1968. Which team provided the opposition?

MISCELLANEOUS (4)

941 At the start of 1981/82 season Liverpool had four players on their books not born in the UK or Ireland. Can you name them?

942 Who did Liverpool play in Ron Yeats's Testimonial?

943 Where was the 1966 Charity Shield against Everton played?

944 Who did Liverpool play in Phil Neal's 400th match for the club?

945 In 1960/61 Liverpool beat Nantes of France in which trophy?

946 The record Merseyside derby crowd was at Goodison in 1948. How close can you get to it?

947 When was the first time the first division championship trophy passed from Everton to Liverpool?

948 Steve Nicol played his first senior game for Ayr United in 1979. Who were Ayr playing?

949 Who played in both the Billy Liddell and Steve Heighway testimonials and scored?

950 Who took over as captain of Liverpool from Phil Thompson?

951 To which team did David Fairclough go on loan in April 1982?

952 Where was Mark Lawrenson born?

953 When England won the 1982 Under 21 European championship who captained the team?

954 Which famous Liverpool keeper once lost seven goals in a senior game?

955 Which famous comedian was once on Liverpool's books?

956 Which Liverpool player went to Bristol Rovers in part exchange for Phil Taylor?

957 Who was the last amateur to play for the Reds in the 1950s?

958 The 1914 Cup final, Liverpool's first, was also a first for what other great British institution?

959 When reserve player Mick Halsall left Anfield, where did he go?

960 In the 1984 Milk Cup final replay, which Liverpool player made his 550th appearance for the club?

REDS IN THE LEAGUE CUP (3)

961 In 1970/71 the Reds lost 0-2 in round three to which previous League Cup winners?

962 When Liverpool lost the 1978 final to Forest in a replay, where did it take place?

963 In the second round of the 1979/80 Cup who held Liverpool to a 0-0 draw in the second round only to lose the replay 4-0?

964 At the start of their four consecutive Cup wins in 1980/81 who did Liverpool beat 4-1 on aggregate?

965 Name the keeper who played in the second round against Carlisle in 1972/73 in a 1-1 draw.

966 In the 1982 final against Spurs who scored for Liverpool with three minutes left to put the game into extra time?

967 In the 1984 final replay, who got the crucial goal against Everton?

968 In 1985/86 the Reds beat Oldham 3-0 in the second round first leg at Anfield. Who got a double on his League Cup debut?

969 What was the aggregate score in the second round of the 1982/83 Cup against Ipswich?

970 In the second round of the 1984/85 Cup who made his debut against Stockport as a substitute for Kenny Dalglish?

971 Who put the Reds out of the 1975/76 Cup?

972 In 1980/81 who did Liverpool beat at Anfield by 5-0 in the second round?

973 In the 1978 semi-final against Arsenal what was the score at Highbury in the second leg?

974 In the fourth round of the 1973/74 Cup Liverpool beat Hull City 3-1 after a 0-0 draw. Who got a hat-trick for the Reds in that game?

975 Who drew 2-2 at Anfield in the fourth round in 1977/78 but lost 2-0 to the Reds on their own patch?

976 In 1981-82 in the fourth round Liverpool won 3-0 after a drawn match. All the goals came in extra time in the replay. Name the opposition and the three goal heroes?

977 In the 1982 final which players got the extra-time goals in the 3-1 victory?

978 Who did Liverpool beat in the 1983 final?

979 In 1983-84 who did Liverpool beat 8-1 on aggregate in the second round?

980 In the fourth round of the 1985/86 competition, Liverpool beat Manchester United 2-1. Who got the double for the Reds?

THE LEAGUE CAMPAIGNS (6)

981 In 1982/83, although they won the League, Liverpool only scored four goals in the last six weeks of the League. Who got three of them?

982 The top League scorer of 1970/71 only got ten goals, but he only played in 21 matches. Who?

983 When Liverpool won the league in 1973 who were second?

984 Who made his League debut at Anfield in the last game of the 1974/75 League season against QPR, wearing a number 9 jersey?

985 In 1903/04 a winger was Liverpool's top League scorer with ten goals. Who was he?

986 When the Reds won the 1905 second division, who was the goalkeeper who played in all their games?

987 In September 1898 what did Liverpool achieve by beating Everton 2-0?

988 Who hit four goals in two matches in the first five weeks of the 1927/28 season?

989 In 1982/83 Graeme Souness missed one League match at Brighton. Who wore the number 11 jersey in that match?

990 Who was the top League scorer in 1985?

991 Who was second-top League scorer in 1986 behind Ian Rush?

992 When Liverpool won the title in 1976 and 1977, name the two teams who were joint second?

993 In 1927 Liverpool played which famous team for the first time in the first division and beat them 8-2?

994 On Christmas Day and Boxing Day 1928 Liverpool met the same team and went from losing 2-3 to winning 8-0. Who were they?

995 Name the player who scored Liverpool's two goals the first time they won at Goodison in 1898?

996 What was significant about the crowd when Liverpool beat Everton at Goodison in 1910?

997 In season 1983/84 he chalked up 365 consecutive League appearances for Liverpool. Who?

998 Kenny Dalglish hit his first League hat-trick at Anfield at the end of season 1977/78 against which team?

999 Considered two of Liverpool's best ever goalkeepers, what astonishing League record did Arthur Riley and Elisha Scott manage to set up between them in the five years from 1929-34?

1000 Name the forward who played all 42 League games in the title-winning team of 1922 and never scored a goal?

1001 Laurie Hughes played in 303 League games and scored one goal. Who was his goal against?

Answers

1 ~~Kenny Dalglish.~~ *Ian Rush.*
2 Leicester.
3 John McGregor.
4 Mike Newall of Luton.
5 Motherwell.
6 Luton Town.
7 ~~£50,000.~~ *£700,000.*
8 Leicester City.
9 Tottenham Hotspur.
10 They hit a record aggregate score of 13-2 against Fulham.
11 Gary Gillespie, who was called up for Scotland to replace Alan Hansen.
12 Newcastle.
13 7-2.
14 Oxford United.
15 Norwich City.
16 Falkirk.
17 Mike Hooper.
18 Manchester City.
19 Geoff Twentyman, Ron Yeats.
20 Jan Molby.

SOME CLUB FACTS
ANSWERS

21 Peter Robinson.
22 61,905 v Wolves in 1952.
23 11-0 against Stromsgodset in the 1974 Cup Winners Cup.
24 1-9 against Birmingham.
25 Ian Callaghan.
26 88 in 1985/86.
27 106 in 1895/96.
28 1965.
29 1900/01.
30 1981.
31 1964/65.

32 W E Barclay.

33 1977.

34 Eight.

35 1894/95.

36 16.

37 ~~Ten.~~ Eleven.

38 Higher Walton.

39 1914, 1950, 1971, 1977.

40 Southampton, in 1985/86.

REDS IN EUROPE (1)
ANSWERS

41 Lech Poznan.

42 Graeme Souness, Terry McDermott.

43 Eintracht, in the 1972/73 Cup Winners Cup.

44 Ian Callaghan.

45 Gordon Wallace.

46 Dundalk, 1969/70 Fairs Cup.

47 Phil Neal.

48 Barcelona.

49 Tommy Smith, Geoff Strong.

50 Ferencvaros, 1967/68 Cup Winners Cup.

51 Inter Milan.

52 Petrolui Ploesti.

53 TSV Munich 1860.

54 Peter Wall.

55 4-0.

56 He scored in every round.

57 Gerry Byrne, Gordon Milne.

58 Ron Yeats.

59 Atletico Bilbao, in the 1968/69 Fairs Cup.

60 Cologne.

WHERE DID THEY COME FROM? (1)
ANSWERS

61 Partick Thistle.

62 Lochgelly Violet.

63 Everton.

64 Nottingham Forest.

65 Dick White.

66 Northampton.

67 Broadway Utd.

68 Bolton.

69 Stoke City.

70 Chelsea, £96,000.

71 Ray Kennedy, from Arsenal.

72 Paisley Abercorn.

73 Bury.

74 Bristol Rovers.

75 Birmingham City.

76 Partick Thistle.

77 Manchester City.

78 Preston North End.

79 South Liverpool.

80 David Johnson, from Ipswich.

WHERE DID THEY GO? (I)
ANSWERS

81 St Mirren.

82 Harry Chambers.

83 Middlesbrough.

84 Bolton.

85 Sampdoria, £650,000.

86 Burnley.

87 Ballymena.

88 Prescott Cables.

89 Maccabi Tel Aviv.

90 He became a Presbyterian Minister.

91 He joined Portsmouth, managed by Ian St John.

92 Sunderland.

93 1964 for £55,000 to Wolves.

94 Glasgow Rangers.

95 Weymouth.

96 1967.

97 Blackburn Rovers.

98 Colchester.
99 Dick Forshaw.
100 Plymouth, Burnley.

101 Luton Town at Anfield.
102 Southampton.
103 Graeme Souness.
104 Kenny Dalglish.
105 Newcastle.
106 Mark Lawrenson.
107 Brentford.
108 Sheffield Wednesday.
109 Coventry at Anfield.
110 Brighton (0-2).
111 Ronnie Whelan.
112 Mike Robinson, Steve Nicol.
113 Against Norwich in the last League match of the season.
114 Meadow Lane against Notts County.
115 Graeme Souness.
116 Fulham.
117 3-0.
118 Souness and Dalglish with seven apiece.
119 John Wark.
120 Grobbelaar, Neal, Kennedy, Lawrenson, Whelan, Hansen, Dalglish, Lee, Rush, Johnston, Souness.

121 Kevin Keegan.
122 Scunthorpe.
123 1971.
124 Wales.

125 Grimsby.

126 Alex Raisbeck and Sailor Hunter.

127 Barnsley St Peters.

128 Four times.

129 Everton.

130 Ronnie Orr.

131 Newtown.

132 Eph Longworth.

133 Harry Bradshaw.

134 Bramall Lane.

135 Derby.

136 West Brom, Nottingham Forest.

137 Percy Saul.

138 Millwall.

139 Sam Raybould.

140 Northwich Victoria.

141 Bristol City.

142 Sam Raybould.

143 Derby.

144 Preston North End.

145 Frank McGarvey.

146 Wales, in 1971.

147 Phil Neal, Phil Thompson, Ray Kennedy.

148 Sammy Lee.

149 Against East Germany in 1977.

150 Seven.

151 Minnesota Kicks.

152 Yugoslavia in 1982. He was then with Chelsea.

153 China.

154 Matt Busby.

155 George Allan in 1897.
156 Jimmy Melia.
157 Chris Lawler.
158 Ian Callaghan, who won 2 caps in 1966 and two in 1977.
159 Denmark.
160 None.
161 He kept goal in nine consecutive games for England.
162 Harry Bradshaw.
163 Alan A'Court.
164 Ray Clemence, Kevin Keegan.

THE LEAGUE CAMPAIGNS (I)
ANSWERS

165 Middlesbrough.
166 Southampton.
167 Johnny Wheeler.
168 Jimmy Greaves.
169 45 (in 1900/01).
170 Brighton.
171 Nottingham Forest.
172 Paul Barron and Mark Grew.
173 Southampton.
174 Wolves.
175 97.
176 Kevin Lewis.
177 Manchester United.
178 Derek Brownbill.
179 David Fairclough.
180 Sammy Lee.
181 16.
182 William Devlin.
183 Fourth.
184 The Lancashire District League.

185 Tony McNamara.

186 Phil Neal.

187 Joe Mercer.

188 At Middlesbrough in August 1977.

189 Billy Liddell.

190 In the 1978 European Cup final against Bruges.

191 Phil Neal.

192 Bertie Vogts.

193 Alfons Bastijns.

194 Ernst Happel.

195 Alun Evans.

196 He played in a winning Middlesbrough team at Anfield.

197 Alan Hansen.

198 Policeman.

199 Phil Thompson.

200 Frank McGarvey.

201 Spurs in the FA Cup in 1980.

202 Terry McDermott, Kenny Dalglish, David Johnson.

203 Bill Shankly, of course.

204 Phil Boersma.

REDS IN THE LEAGUE CUP (I)
ANSWERS

205 Tommy Leishman.

206 Alec Lindsay.

207 Kenny Dalglish.

208 Ray Kennedy, Jimmy Case.

209 Exeter City.

210 0-1.

211 Kenny Dalglish.

212 Exeter City (again).

213 4-2.

214 Rotherham, Craig Johnston.

215 Ronnie Whelan.

216 Birmingham and Sheffield Wednesday.

217 Tottenham.

218 5-2.

219 Paul Goddard.

220 Portsmouth.

221 Queens Park Rangers.

222 Southampton.

223 Mansfield.

224 Carlisle (away from home in a 1-1 draw).

225 Ian Rush.

226 £300,000.

227 1980.

228 Scotland.

229 Fourteen.

230 5-0.

231 Roger Hunt.

232 Siggi Held.

233 Ron Yeats.

234 Gerry Byrne.

235 Alf Arrowsmith.

236 Chelsea.

237 Geoff Strong.

238 He won a World Cup winners medal.

239 Billy Stevenson.

240 Phil Chisnall.

241 Standard Liege at Anfield.

242 West Ham.

243 Gordon Milne.

244 Sheffield United.

245 Chelsea.

246 Chris Lawler, Geoff Strong.

247 Northampton.

248 Lawrence, Lawler, Byrne, Milne, Yeats, Stevenson, Callaghan, Hunt, St John, Smith, Thompson.

REDS IN EUROPE (2) ANSWERS

249 Rotterdam.

250 10-0.

251 Ajax Amsterdam.

252 Sandro Mazzola.

253 Hampden Park.

254 Malmo, in the 1967/68 Fairs Cup.

255 Juventus.

256 Borussia Dortmund.

257 Tony Hateley.

258 0-1.

259 Atletico Bilbao.

260 Phil Chisnall.

261 Chris Lawler, Ian St John.

262 Alex Lindsay.

263 Bayern Munich.

264 John Toshack.

265 Ray Kennedy, Jimmy Case, Kevin Keegan.

266 Servette Geneva.

267 The UEFA Cup, in 1973.

268 Steve Peplow.

REDS IN THE FA CUP (2) INTO THE FIFTIES ANSWERS

269 Arsenal.

270 Wolves.

271 Goodison Park (Old Trafford was still under repair from bombing).

272 Bob Paisley.

273 Ray Lewis.

274 White Hart Lane.

275 Cardiff, Birmingham, and Chelsea.

276 Everton.

277 The matches were two-leg affairs.

278 South Shields.

279 It was Liverpool's first Wembley Cup final.

280 4-0.

281 Freeman.

282 Burnley.

283 Barnsley.

284 Newcastle.

285 Tranmere Rovers.

286 Blackburn Rovers.

287 Southampton.

288 Yeovil & Petters.

THE LEAGUE CAMPAIGNS (2)
ANSWERS

289 At West Bromwich.

290 11.

291 Everton, Coventry.

292 Tottenham.

293 Leicester City.

294 Twenty games.

295 It was a record tenth title.

296 Everton (0-2).

297 3-1.

298 Steve Bruce in a 3-3 draw.

299 QPR, Leeds, West Bromwich and Everton.

300 Stoke City.

301 Sunderland.

302 Old Trafford.

303 Steve Nicol.

304 Their last seven matches.

305 Pat Gordon, Harry Bradshaw.

306 Robert Robinson.

307 Billy Stevenson.

308 Phil Neal.

309 Craig Johnston.
310 South Africa.
311 Middlesbrough.
312 Australia.

313 Terry McDermott (13).
314 Fifth.
315 Ipswich in the number seven jersey.
316 Sammy Lee.
317 Ray Kennedy.
318 Bayern Munich, in the semi-final of the European Cup.
319 Avi Cohen.
320 Colin Russell.
321 Bradford City.
322 Colin Irwin, Richard Money, Howard Gayle.
323 Stoke City.
324 Terry McDermott.
325 Steve Heighway.
326 Ray Kennedy.
327 Altrincham.
328 Birmingham.
329 Kevin Sheedy.
330 It was the first League match he had missed since joining Liverpool.
331 Alan Kennedy.
332 Everton.

333 He never officially held the job.

334 George Kaye.

335 Phil Taylor.

336 Alan Jones.

337 None.

338 Kenny Dalglish!

339 Rochdale.

340 345.

341 Cumbernauld.

342 Matt McQueen.

343 Tom Watson.

344 George Kaye.

345 Don Welsh.

346 Carlisle, Grimsby, Workington, Huddersfield.

347 Ray Kennedy.

348 Six times.

349 He won three major trophies (League, League Cup, European Cup).

350 Charlie Wilson.

351 Headmaster.

352 John Houlding.

SOME EARLY HISTORY
ANSWERS

353 October 13 1894 at Goodison.

354 Crystal Palace.

355 Matt McQueen.

356 Goalkeeper William McOwen.

357 King John of Everton.

358 The Lancashire League Trophy, The Liverpool District Cup.

359 Bootle.

360 They went through the campaign undefeated.

361 Newton Heath (now Manchester United).

362 Stoke City (2-0).

363 Blackburn Rovers.
364 Harry Bradshaw.
365 Malcolm McVean.
366 0-3.
367 September 1897.
368 Grimsby.
369 Middlesbrough Ironopolis.
370 Aston Villa.
371 10-1 against Rotherham.
372 Arsenal, 5-0.

PICTURE QUIZ (4) ANSWERS

373 Kenny Dalglish.
374 100.
375 Cumbernauld.
376 Jock Stein.

REDS IN EUROPE (3) ANSWERS

376 Emlyn Hughes.
378 0-2.
379 Brian Hall.
380 John Toshack.
381 Atletico Bilbao, Geoff Strong.
382 Bayern Munich.
383 Dinamo Berlin, Dinamo Dresden.
384 Jeunesse D'Esche.
385 9-1.
386 FC Zurich.
387 Bily Stevenson, for Tony Hateley v Munich 1860.
388 John Toshack, Phil Thompson.
389 Leeds.
390 Red Star Belgrade.
391 Ferencvaros.

392 Ian Ross.

393 Servette Geneva.

394 Kevin Keegan (2), Larry Lloyd.

395 Rome.

396 Steve Heighway.

397 Middlesbrough.

398 Bury, for £8,000.

399 Tranmere Rovers.

400 1969, £68,000.

401 Billy Stevenson, Glasgow Rangers.

402 £110,000 in 1970.

403 Stoke City.

404 Wolves.

405 He walked into Anfield and asked for a trial.

406 Coventry, in 1983.

407 Blackpool, £65,000.

408 £300,000.

409 Hamilton Academicals.

410 Ayr United.

411 January 1978.

412 Home Farm.

413 Hibs.

414 Cambuslang.

415 £900,000 to Brighton.

416 Chesterfield.

417 Jock McNab.

418 Coventry City, 1974.

419 Birmingham.

420 Middlesbrough.

421 Belfast Celtic.

422 St Mirren, Leeds United.

423 Chester.

424 Real Sociedad.

425 £380,000.

426 He went back to Wrexham.

427 Aston Villa.

428 Tranmere Rovers.

429 Manchester United.

430 Doncaster.

431 Coventry.

432 Bolton.

433 Third Lanark.

434 1981.

435 Coventry, 1972.

436 Minnesota Kicks.

PICTURE QUIZ (5)
ANSWERS

437 Graeme Souness.

438 Glasgow Rangers.

439 Sampdoria.

440 European Cup medal.

REMEMBER THIS SEASON—1922/23
ANSWERS

441 Harry Chambers.

442 Dick Johnson.

443 Arsenal.

444 Dick Forshaw.

445 Bootle.

446 Wolves.

447 Donald McKinlay.

448 Sheffield United.

449 John McNab.

450 Tommy Lucas.

451 Danny Shone.

452 Stoke City.

453 Harry Chambers.

454 Cyril Gilhespy.

455 Sheffield United.

456 106,000.

457 Tom Bromilow.

458 21 (exactly half).

459 Fire broke out in the stand.

460 Dick Forshaw.

REDS IN THE FA CUP (3)
THE BUILDING YEARS
ANSWERS

461 Gateshead.

462 Southend.

463 Antonio Rowley, Dick White and John Molyneux.

464 Worcester City.

465 Roger Hunt and Ian St John (who else?).

466 West Ham.

467 Bournemouth, Walsall, Spurs, West Brom (lost in second replay).

468 John McLaughlin.

469 Leicester at Hillsborough.

470 Steve Heighway.

471 Roger Hunt.

472 Chelsea 2-0.

473 Stockport.

474 Preston North End.

475 Watford.

476 Swansea.

477 Over 40,000 saw the match at Anfield on closed circuit TV.

478 Ronnie Moran.

479 Leicester City.

480 Chelsea.

481 65.

482 Ronnie Orr.

483 28.

484 Oxford United.

485 David Johnson.

486 At Newcastle.

487 Nine (in 1953/54).

488 Sheffield Wednesday.

489 Alf Arrowsmith.

490 Derby County.

491 Alan Hansen.

492 8-0.

493 James Harrop.

494 Nine.

495 Willie Carlin, Reg Blore.

496 Bobby Graham.

497 Avi Cohen.

498 David Fairclough.

499 Everton.

500 It was the first time apart from Goodison Liverpool had played in front of over 40,000.

501 Goalkeeper David Harvey.

502 Tony MacNamara with Everton, Liverpool, Crewe and Bury.

503 Cliff Lloyd.

504 Henry Lowe.

505 Dunfermline.

506 Arthur Riley.

507 St Asaph.

508 Chesterfield, New Brighton, Ilkeston Town.

509 Everton.

510 Hibernian.

511 Hetton-Le-Hole.

512 The number four.
513 The team were all Scots.
514 Cyril Cambridge.
515 1952.
516 Stan Cullis.
517 Drumchapel Amateurs.
518 None.
519 James Harley.
520 Phil Neal.

PICTURE QUIZ (6) ANSWERS

521 Phil Thompson.
522 1971.
523 Coventry.
524 The 1974 FA Cup final.

REMEMBER THIS SEASON—1976/77 ANSWERS

525 Manchester City.
526 Everton.
527 West Bromwich.
528 Aston Villa (3-0, all goals coming in the last 14 minutes).
529 Crusaders.
530 Manchester United.
531 Alan Simonsen.
532 Phil Neal, Emlyn Hughes.
533 David Johnson.
534 6-1.
535 Jimmy Case.
536 Crystal Palace.
537 3-0.
538 Jimmy Case.
539 David Fairclough.
540 Manchester United, May 1977 in a 1-0 win.
541 Aston Villa.

542 Alec Lindsay.

543 David Johnson.

544 Clemence, Neal, Jones, Smith, Kennedy, Hughes, Keegan, Case, Heighway, Callaghan, McDermott.

REDS IN EUROPE (4)
ANSWERS

545 Vitoria Setubal.

546 St Etienne.

547 Brian Kettle, Maxwell Thompson.

548 Ferencvaros, in the 1970/71 Fairs Cup.

549 Hibernian.

550 Chris Lawler.

551 Kevin Keegan.

552 Willie Miller of Aberdeen.

553 Alan Waddle.

554 Ray Kennedy.

555 8-0.

556 Phil Neal.

557 Terry McDermott, Tommy Smith, Phil Neal.

558 Borussia Munchengladbach.

559 JK Helsinki.

560 Rainer Bonhof.

561 Oulu Palloseura in the 1981/82 European Cup at Anfield.

562 Dinamo Bucharest.

563 Jimmy Case.

564 Dinamo Tiblisi (2-4 aggregate).

INTERNATIONAL REDS (2)
ANSWERS

565 Larry Lloyd.

566 Jim Beglin, Mark Lawrenson, Ronnie Whelan.

567 Argentina.

568 He played 14 consecutive games in goal.

569 Brazil.

570 His brother Billy.

571 Jan Molby and Steve Nicol.

572 Rumania.

573 Ian Callaghan against France.

574 Stan Bowles.

575 Rumania.

576 Jimmy MacDougall.

577 Argentina.

578 Austria.

579 True (53).

580 Against Hungary in Budapest (3-1).

581 Clemence, Neal, McDermott, Hughes, Keegan, R Kennedy, Callaghan.

582 Steve Foster.

583 Billy Dunlop.

584 Against England at Wembley.

PICTURE QUIZ (7) ANSWERS

585 Emlyn Hughes.

586 Crazy Horse.

587 Blackpool.

588 Rotherham.

THE LEAGUE CAMPAIGNS (4) ANSWERS

588 Sheffield Wednesday and Everton.

589 Lawrence, Lawler, Lloyd, Lindsay, Livermore.

591 Spurs.

592 31 (ten played six or less games).

593 Bill Shankly was appointed manager.

594 Sheffield United.

595 David Fairclough.

596 Kevin Keegan.

597 John Evans.

598 Eighth.

599 All eleven of them.
600 George Allan.
601 Duncan McLean.
602 Leicester.
603 1905/06.
604 Dave Wilson.
605 Eight times.
606 Leyton Orient.
607 Five.
608 West Bromwich Albion.

REMEMBER THIS SEASON—1972/73
ANSWERS

609 He only played in just over half the games.
610 Eintracht Frankfurt.
611 Seven seasons.
612 Emlyn Hughes.
613 Frank Lane.
614 Kevin Keegan against Eintracht.
615 All six of them.
616 Steve Heighway (by Hall then Boersma).
617 Manchester City.
618 Peter Cormack.
619 Carlisle.
620 Hughes (2), Boersma.
621 Phil Thompson.
622 Kevin Keegan.
623 Phil Boersma.
624 Arsenal (0-2).
625 Burnley.
626 Tottenham.
627 Trevor Storton.
628 Leeds United, in a replay, of course.

629 Ray Clemence.
630 £15,000.
631 Swansea.
632 Three.

REDS IN EUROPE (5)
ANSWERS

633 It was the first one decided on penalty kicks.
634 Aberdeen.
635 David Johnson.
636 Benfica at Anfield 1977/78.
637 Alan Kennedy.
638 Ian Rush.
639 Benfica.
640 In the semi-final of the 1978 European Cup against Borussia Munchengladbach.
641 Trabzonspor and St Etienne.
642 Graeme Souness.
643 Ronnie Whelan.
644 Alan Hansen, Kenny Dalglish.
645 AZ'67 Alkmaar.
646 BK Odense in 1983.
647 Kenny Dalglish.
648 6-1.
649 Widzew Lodz.
650 0-2, Nottingham Forest.
651 Rome.
652 Bayern Munich in the 1981 European Cup semi-final.

REMEMBER THIS SEASON 1961/62
ANSWERS

653 99.

654 Chelsea.

655 Alf Arrowsmith.

656 Jim Furnell.

657 Byrne, Milne, Melia and A'Court.

658 41 (in 41 games).

659 Middlesbrough.

660 Tommy Leishman.

661 Ian Callaghan.

662 Ian St John.

663 Austria.

664 Kevin Lewis.

665 Leeds, Walsall, Swansea, Middlesbrough, Bury.

666 Ron Yeats.

667 Johnny Wheeler.

668 Preston.

669 Old Trafford.

670 Swansea.

671 Rotherham.

672 He was an established Scotland international going to play in the second division.

REDS IN THE FA CUP (4)
THE SEVENTIES
ANSWERS

673 Steve Heighway.

674 Newcastle.

675 Middlesbrough.

676 Old Trafford (0-0) Villa Park (3-1).

677 Southend.

678 Kenny Dalglish.

679 Peter Thompson.

680 Alun Evans and Brian Hall.

681 Carlisle.

682 Ipswich.

683 David Johnson.

684 Graeme Souness.

685 Oxford United.
686 John Toshack.
687 Manchester United.
688 Derby.
689 Alan Hansen.
690 Ian Callaghan.
691 Doncaster.
692 Terry McDermott.

693 Gordon Milne.
694 Gary Sprake of Wales.
695 Spain at Hampden in 1984.
696 He wore the number seven jersey for the only time.
697 Saudi Arabia.
698 Tommy Miller, who got two against England in 1920.
699 Phil Neal.
700 In Amsterdam against Holland.
701 Maurice Parry 1901.
702 None.
703 Steve Coppell.
704 Alan Kennedy.
705 Kenneth Campbell, Tommy Younger, Tommy Lawrence.
706 Hampden Park against Scotland in 1980.
707 Ian St John.
708 Harry Chambers in 1921.
709 Ray Kennedy.
710 Laurie Hughes.
711 Gerry Byrne.
712 Mexico (1) France (2).

713 Gordon Hodgson.
714 South Africa.

715 36.

716 Cricket.

MISCELLANEOUS (3)
ANSWERS

717 Copa De Los Libertores.

718 Inverness Caley.

719 Gordon Milne.

720 Wayne Harrison.

721 Joe Harvey.

722 Alan A'Court.

723 Alan Kennedy.

724 Ipswich, in 1985.

725 Denis Mortimer.

726 Chairman of the Sports Council.

727 1973.

728 Alan Kennedy.

729 George Kaye.

730 Crystal Palace.

731 Aston Villa.

732 Bayern Munich, in the semi-final of the European Cup.

733 At Goodison against Everton.

734 Colin Irwin.

735 He scored with a penalty!

736 Preston.

REDS IN THE LEAGUE CUP (2)
ANSWERS

737 5-2.

738 Sheffield United.

739 West Bromwich.

740 Kenny Dalglish, Ray Kennedy.

741 Sheffield United.

742 Manchester City.

743 Norwich.

744 Carlisle, West Bromwich, Leeds, Tottenham.

745 David Fairclough.

746 John Robertson (penalty).
747 Steve McMahon, Craig Johnston.
748 Burnley.
749 Barnsley.
750 Fulham.
751 Villa Park.
752 David Fairclough.
753 Chelsea.
754 Middlesbrough (0-1).
755 Chris Lawler.
756 Bolton.

THE LEAGUE CAMPAIGNS (5) ANSWERS

757 Bury.
758 Malcolm McVean.
759 0-5.
760 Arsenal, Huddersfield.
761 Seventh.
762 The biggest ever crowd at Goodison (78,599).
763 Leeds United.
764 Bobby Graham.
765 Nottingham Forest.
766 Four.
767 13.
768 Middlesbrough.
769 Sam Raybould.
770 William Perkins.
771 11th.
772 Portsmouth, Manchester United, West Bromwich.
773 Third.
774 John Molyneux.
775 Swansea.
776 David Fairclough.

777 Matt McQueen.

778 12.

779 Glenbuck.

780 Nine seasons.

781 Altrincham, Nelson.

782 Steve McMahon.

783 David Ashworth.

784 Tom Watson.

785 Oldham, Manchester City, Stockport.

786 Southampton.

787 Phil Taylor.

788 1st December 1959.

789 Manchester City, Bradford.

790 Tom Watson.

791 George Patterson.

792 Don Welsh.

793 George Kaye.

794 Bill Shankly.

795 Dave Hickson.

796 David Ashworth.

PICTURE QUIZ(10)
ANSWERS

797 Roger Hunt.

798 1959.

799 34.

800 Bolton Wanderers.

REDS IN THE LEAGUE
SOME FIRSTS—AND LASTS
ANSWERS

801 Keith Burkinshaw.

802 Albert Stubbins.

803 West Bromwich.

804 Middlesbrough.

805 Matt McQueen.

806 At Fulham, wearing number 10.

807 Wolves.

808 Left-back.

809 Southampton.

810 Derby.

811 Ipswich.

812 At Newcastle.

813 Tommy Lawrence.

814 Chelsea.

815 Chelsea.

816 15th.

817 Gordon Milne.

818 Bristol Rovers.

819 Charlie Ashcroft.

820 Matt Busby.

REDS IN EUROPE (6)
ANSWERS

821 Jim Beglin.

822 Panathanaikos.

823 Steve Nicol.

824 Jim Beglin in 1985 against Panathanaikos.

825 Gary Gillespie.

826 John Wark against Lech Poznan.

827 At Easter Road, Edinburgh, against Hibs in 1975/76.

828 Terry McDermott.

829 Phil Neal, Graeme Souness, Ian Rush, Alan Kennedy.

830 Nottingham Forest in the 1978/79 European Cup at Anfield.

831 0-1.

832 He appeared as a substitute for Dalglish in the European Cup semi-final against Munchengladbach and was later substituted himself by Jimmy Case.
833 John Wark.
834 Anderlecht.
835 Ian Rush.
836 17.
837 Mark Lawrenson.
838 David Fairclough.
839 Austria Vienna.
840 0-2.

WHERE DID THEY COME FROM? (3) ANSWERS

841 Maccabi Tel Aviv, 1979.
842 Wrexham.
843 Blackpool.
844 Sunderland.
845 Glasgow Rangers.
846 Ron Yeats, from Dundee United.
847 Bristol Rovers, for £60,000.
848 Fred Pagnam.
849 Arsenal.
850 Carlisle.
851 Scunthorpe, of course.
852 Manchester United.
853 Wolves, for £100,000 in 1968.
854 Archie & Billy Goldie.
855 Aberdeen.
856 Johnny Wheeler.
857 Celtic.
858 Ian St John, Motherwell.
859 Newcastle.
860 Gordon Milne.

861 Southend.

862 Stoke City.

863 Sunderland.

864 Basle.

865 Swansea.

866 Everton, of all places.

867 Swansea.

868 Sheffield United.

869 Falkirk.

870 Arthur Goddard.

871 Bristol City.

872 Coventry, £75,000.

873 Swansea.

874 Leeds United.

875 New Brighton.

876 Partick Thistle and Hamilton Accies.

877 Tranmere Rovers.

878 Bolton.

879 Bristol City.

880 West Bromwich Albion.

REMEMBER THIS SEASON—1946/47
ANSWERS

881 Blackpool.

882 Portsmouth, Derby, Arsenal.

883 Bob Paisley.

884 Bill Watkinson.

885 Blackpool (2-3).

886 Ewood Park, Blackburn.

887 Len Carney.

888 Seven.

889 Chelsea.

890 Cyril Sidlow.

891 Phil Taylor.

892 Birmingham City.

893 Jack Balmer, Albert Stubbins.
894 Harry Eastham.
895 Derby.
896 Cyril Sidlow, Ray Minshull, Charlie Ashcroft.
897 Jack Balmer.
898 Maine Road.
899 Harold Kaye.
900 Derby County.

REDS IN THE FA CUP (5)
THE EIGHTIES
ANSWERS

901 Ian Rush (2), Craig Johnston.
902 Jimmy Case.
903 Kevin MacDonald.
904 Brighton.
905 Craig Johnston.
906 David Johnson.
907 Norwich.
908 Swansea.
909 Altrincham.
910 McGrath (og).
911 Gary Gillespie.
912 York City.
913 Spurs, Terry McDermott.
914 Southampton, White Hart Lane.
915 John Wark.
916 Hillsborough, Villa Park (2), Highfield Road.
917 Ronnie Whelan and Paul Walsh.
918 Barnsley.
919 York, again!
920 Jan Molby.

INTERNATIONAL REDS (4)
ANSWERS

921 John Toshack.
922 They were all against foreign opposition away from home.

923 Wales (5-3) in 1969.

924 Austria in Vienna (4-1).

925 In New York against the USA.

926 Ernest Peake against England in 1913.

927 Salonika, Greece.

928 Phil Thompson.

929 Sam Hardy in 1909 against Hungary in Budapest.

930 Norway (4-0).

931 In New York against Italy in 1976.

932 It was the first floodlit international at Wembley.

933 England, in Sheffield.

934 He wore the number nine shirt.

935 Ray Lambert in 1949 against Portugal.

936 Billy Lacey 1913.

937 Sweden in 1947.

938 Bill Jones.

939 Yugoslavia.

940 Sweden.

MISCELLANEOUS (4)
ANSWERS

941 Bruce Grobbelaar (South Africa), Avi Cohen (Israel), Craig Johnston (Australia), Tony Bredbury (Hong Kong).

942 Glasgow Celtic.

943 Goodison Park.

944 Exeter City in the 1981 League Cup.

945 The Friendship Cup.

946 78,299.

947 Everton won it in 1939 and Liverpool took it in 1947.

948 Arbroath.

949 Dave Hickson!

950 Graeme Souness.

951 Toronto Blizzard.

952 Preston.

953 Sammy Lee.

954 Ray Clemence (then with Scunthorpe).

955 Stan Boardman.

956 Ted Harthill.

957 Doug Rudham.

958 The Monarchy. King George V attended the final for the first time.

959 Birmingham.

960 Phil Neal.

961 Swindon.

962 Old Trafford.

963 Tranmere.

964 Bradford City.

965 Frank Lane.

966 Ronnie Whelan.

967 Graeme Souness.

968 Steve McMahon.

969 4-1.

970 Jan Molby.

971 Burnley, 1-0.

972 Swindon.

973 0-0.

974 Ian Callaghan.

975 Coventry.

976 Arsenal, Craig Johnston, Terry McDermott, Kenny Dalglish.

977 Ronnie Whelan, Ian Rush.

978 Manchester United.

979 Brentford.

980 Jan Molby.

THE LEAGUE CAMPAIGNS (6)
ANSWERS

981 Craig Johnston.

982 Alun Evans.

983 Arsenal.

984 Jimmy Case.

985 Jack Cox.

986 Teddy Doig.

987 It was Liverpool's first win at Goodison.
988 William Devlin.
989 Mark Lawrenson.
990 John Wark (18).
991 Jan Molby.
992 Queens Park Rangers, Manchester City.
993 Portsmouth.
994 Burnley.
995 Andrew McCowie.
996 It was the first time Liverpool had played in front of over 50,000.
997 Phil Neal.
998 Manchester City.
999 They lost 428 goals between them.
1000 Fred Hopkin.
1001 Preston North End.